Children of the Salmon
and Other Irish Folktales

Books by Eileen O'Faolain

IRISH SAGAS AND FOLK-TALES

CHILDREN OF THE SALMON AND OTHER
IRISH FOLKTALES

Children of the Salmon
and Other Irish Folktales

SELECTIONS AND TRANSLATIONS BY
Eileen O'Faolain

ILLUSTRATED BY
Trina Hyman

An Atlantic Monthly Press Book

LITTLE, BROWN AND COMPANY · BOSTON · TORONTO

Acknowledgment is made to The Royal Bank of Ireland, Ltd.,
Trustee of the Estate of Dr. Douglas Hyde, for permission to use
four stories, "Ceatach and Blackbird," "Paudyeen O'Kelly and
the Weasel," "How the First Cat Was Created" and "The Cat
and the Mouse"; and to Dr. James Delargy, editor of *Béaloideas,*
the Journal of the Folklore of Ireland Society, for permission to
use "Liam Donn" and many other pieces taken from that in-
valuable journal; to Peadar O'Griobhtha, who collected and
wrote down "Liam Donn"; to Pádraig O'Tuathail for permission to use excerpts from *Folktales from Carlow and West
Wicklow;* to Nuala Ni Dubhda for permission to use excerpts
from *Sgéalta Sidhe,* collected by her father, Sean O'Dubhda;
and to Martin Burke for excerpts from *Tipperary Tales.*

ATLANTIC–LITTLE, BROWN BOOKS
ARE PUBLISHED BY
LITTLE, BROWN AND COMPANY
IN ASSOCIATION WITH
THE ATLANTIC MONTHLY PRESS

*Published simultaneously in Canada
by Little, Brown & Company (Canada) Limited*

PRINTED IN THE UNITED STATES OF AMERICA

Preface

I REMEMBER well, as if it were yesterday, though it is many years ago now, for I was only a schoolgirl at the time, spending an entire wet day perched up on the sill of a lobby window looking out over the flooded River Lee, a dreary prospect, and being wafted imperceptibly into what was to me a strange world — the world of Faery, of *Tir na n-Og*. There I sat for hours, my knees under my chin, the book under my nose, wandering to the Eastern World with Finn Mac Cool, Oisin, Oscar and the Fianna, and other champions and warriors of the old Irish world while, with the power of magic or of the faery, they killed giants, outwitted hags, and saved maidens from fearful monsters. The book that brought me into this otherworld was *Beside the Fire,* a book of Irish folktales collected in the west of Ireland from a few old Gaelic speakers by Douglas Hyde, and published by David Nutt (London, 1890). When the light began to pale I closed the book reluctantly, and as I did, I read the dedication on the first page:

"To the memory of those truly cultured and unselfish men, the poet-scribes and hedge-schoolmasters of the last century and the beginning of this — men who may be called the last of the Milesians — I dedicate this effort to preserve even a scrap of that native lore which in their day they loved so passionately, and for the preservation of which they worked so nobly, but in vain."

"In vain" — this death knell might have made the tears flow from my eyes as copiously as the raindrops down the window-pane at my elbow. Sad — sad and dispiriting like the Irish history I was learning at school. "They went forth to battle, but they always fell."

It was many years before I took up Douglas Hyde's *Beside the Fire* again. It was 1940. We in Ireland had meanwhile severed the connection with England, and were now running our own country. I read the angry preface in which, in 1890, he was calling out for help to save a fine folklore that was in danger of being lost through neglect. Some of the tales, he said, were as old as a thousand years and were in danger of dying on the lips of the old Gaelic speakers who alone had them in their memory. "For, of all the traces that man in his earliest period has left behind him, there is nothing but a few drilled stones or flint arrow-heads that approach the antiquity of these tales as told to-day by a half-starving peasant in a smoky Connacht cabin."

In 1940, as I read Douglas Hyde's words of 1890, I can say with truth that tears of joy flowed from my eyes, for not only had our folklore been saved, but it was found to be a folklore rich beyond even Douglas Hyde's wildest imaginings. Fortunately this dedicated man lived on to see, with the founding of the new State, the founding of the Irish Folklore Institute — a group of trained and scientific folklorists, dedicated, like himself, to the task of saving Irish folklore before the last of the Irish speakers had taken their treasure with them to the next world. He had to wait forty years for it — the Irish Folklore Institute was founded in 1926 — but when it came it was the fulfillment of his dream. For now these men of the Irish Folklore Institute, Dr. James H. Delargy, Dr. Sean O'Sullivan and Dr. Thomas Wall and many voluntary helpers, went out to the cottages in the remote Gaelic-speaking parts of Ireland, and took down the stories in Gaelic by their firesides from the lips of the old people, often recording their voices on tape. How could Douglas Hyde, or any of the handful of other enthusiasts like him, have foreseen such a miracle way back in 1890?

The Irish Folklore Institute, now the Irish Folklore Commission, in Dublin, is crammed with folktales, riddles, cures, proverbs, games and folklore of every kind, gathered in so fast and so diligently — even the schoolchildren helped with the collecting — in a race against time before the old Gaelic storytellers died, that there was then no time to catalogue or to sort out a treasury of folklore second to none in Europe.

How much of this Irish folklore has reached the English-speaking public? One might say little or none as yet, for there have been very few translations. The first and the best to date of real Irish folktales in English, apart of course from Douglas Hyde's *Beside the Fire* (London, 1890), are three books by Jeremiah Curtin, *Tales of the Munster Fairies and of the Ghost World* (1895), *Myths and Folklore of Ireland* (1890), and *Hero Tales of Ireland* (1894), and William Larminie's *West Irish Folktales and Romances* (London, 1893).

Curtin, an American folklorist of Irish background, collected the tales in the south of Ireland from Gaelic speakers through an interpreter, and gave what up to then was the best rendering in English of an Irish folktale. Dr. Delargy pronounces them to be "the best ever recorded." Certainly it was an extraordinary *tour de force* for a non-Gaelic speaker, since one might say they have lost little in authenticity, or in fidelity to phrase or language. Dr. Delargy has since published the rest of Curtin's tales, originally printed in the Boston *Sun* around the nineties of the last century.

Before Hyde and Curtin there were no folklorists of the same quality. Samuel Lover, Crofton Croker and Lady Wilde, all writing around the mid-nineteenth century, purported to give the words of the peasant, but in reality their retellings were done at two removes, since they knew neither Gaelic nor the peasant. They were the Ascendancy who peeped out from the drawing room at the peasant and his quaint ways:

"A class," says Yeats in his *Irish Folk and Fairy Tales,* "who never took the populace seriously, and imagined the country as a humourist's Arcadia. Its passion, its gloom, its tragedy they knew nothing of. What they did was wholly false; they merely magnified an irresponsible type, found oftenest among boatmen, car-men, and gentlemen's servants, into the type of a whole nation, and created the stage Irishman. The writers of 'Forty-eight, and the famine, burst their bubble."

Yet, their work had the dash as well as the shallowness of an ascendancy class, and in Croker it is touched everywhere, says Yeats, "with a gentle Arcadian beauty." Among these early anthologists an exception might be made for Patrick Kennedy. He wrote down the stories as he heard them — though not when they were being told, only as he subsequently remembered them — from the lips of the English-speaking peasant of the eastern areas around Dublin known as the Pale, the traditional stronghold of the colonists. The memory of these peasants had grown dim, and the epic quality of the Irish original had become abraded and softened in the tame English retelling. Gone was the salty Gaelic phrase and the direct barbaric incident. In Kennedy's retelling, despite occasional wisps of primeval memory, we find an Irish peasant who has become over-civil. Nevertheless, Patrick Kennedy gave us the real voice of the English-speaking Irish peasant of the Pale, and his stories are the best we have from the 1850's. "We cannot be sure," says Douglas Hyde, always conscious of what the real thing was, "how much belongs to Kennedy the book-seller, and how much to the Wexford peasant."

However, Kennedy did not, like Crofton Croker and Samuel Lover, dress up the tales and rewrite them as "literature." He wrote them from memory as faithfully as he could. What has been lost only those who have read or heard a tale in Gaelic, taken directly from the Irish speaker, can know.

The language of the Gaelic speaker is concrete, common and vivid, as when he says of a landless man: "He hadn't as much land as would choke a worm," or of a hardworking blacksmith: "He had the early blow of a Monday and the late blow of a Saturday," or of a deft fighting man: "He went through his enemies like a hawk through a flock of starlings on a frosty morning." Fine racy talk poured out with energy and imagination.

It may be that this beauty of language and structure is to the scientific folklorist, who regards all folklore as a key to the primitive religion and way of life of primitive man, no more than a by-product. For the rest of us this by-product may be an end in itself. The folktales may to us be the beautiful, unconscious evocation of the life and soul of the people who spoke them and passed them on. For innocence, authenticity and reality, what Robin Flower, speaking of early Irish poetry, calls "chastity of vision," there has never been anything like them. If they are not literature itself, they are the stuff of literature — and the more untampered with the better they are — so that many an artist, the dramatist and poet especially, will read these tales and draw inspiration and sustenance from them in the years to come, returning to them again and again as the salmon returns to the richness and rejuvenation of the eternal sea.

It is a delightful experience to hear a good storyteller telling a tale, or even to hear it over the radio or from a record. It has so much more to it than we can ever guess from the reading — the changing tones of the voice, the dramatic pause, but, above all, the artful handling of the particular devices peculiar to folktales which make altogether for another and a different pleasure. "Such rhetorical devices" writes Dr. Delargy, "as the repetition of incidents, alliteration and rhythm, the characteristic 'runs' which describe vigorous action, and the set openings and endings of tales may appear tame and turgid to the eye of the reader, upon whose ears they would have a very different effect."

Mr. Caoimhin O'Danachair gives the following vivid account of his experiences while recording for the Commission in the south of Ireland:

"The sound-recordings reveal the style of recitation and the atmosphere of the occasion to a marked degree. On a sunny afternoon we recorded a very fine version of Aa. Th. 890, lasting one hour fifteen minutes, from a Kerry story-teller, who, leaning at his ease on a grassy bank in a meadow beside the sea, told the story in quiet, measured tones. On the evening of the same day, in a farmhouse a few miles inland, another story-teller was so carried away by his telling of the hero-tale, *The Well at the World's End,* that he suddenly changed, in the narrative, from the third to the first person and described the hero's adventures as happening to himself, meanwhile striding about the kitchen, waving his arms, while the local collector pursued him with the microphone, and the operator steadied the recording gear on a rickety table and prayed for patience. In the first recording, the level tones of the speaker are heard against a faint background of the beat of the waves on the shore, and the whole impression is one of quiet intensity. In the second, there is an air of bustle and excitement, with sounds of movement and, frequently, the delighted comment of one or other of the audience — which this story-teller expected, and for which he paused at appropriate moments.

"The background noises which find their way into the recordings, and often are not noticed until the replaying, add much to the atmosphere. Noises of the wind and the sea, of crackling fires, of clocks ticking and striking, the cry of animals and even the song of birds are to be heard on many of the recordings; in others a pause in the narration and a greeting tells of the arrival of another member of the audience; we can hear a chair being placed, and the story continues. Thus the atmosphere lives in a way far different from the impression given by any written record."

How much do the Irish still believe in this Faery or otherworld? Or, as Yeats said at the end of the last century, to what extent has what he called "the Spirit of the Age" broken in? In the countryside, especially in the remote Irish-speaking regions, I believe that what I call the Fairy Faith is still intact, in spite of great pretended skepticism. An old woman of my acquaintance, not long dead, used to say: "Yerra, I don't believe in fairies! But," with a quick look over her shoulder she would add, "they're there all right!" I wonder if her daughter-in-law, the new woman in the house, will be one bit surer about their nonexistence, and if the butter fails to churn, or if a cow dies suddenly, I bet a haunted look will steal into her eyes, and that she too, glancing over her shoulder, will lower her voice to talk with respect about The Good People.

"They're all gone these few years back," says another shaky believer. "The motors going up into the mountains have them banished out of it entirely."

But in spite of this brave talk one occasionally finds in the daily papers such news items as that workmen employed by the Land Commission to divide the large estates have refused to take a fence through a "fairy fort," and have had to be permitted to take it maybe twenty or thirty feet out of its line so as not to discommode the "gentry." Or a local council may be asked to remove a council cottage to the other side of the road because, owing to its being built on a "fairy pass," the occupants have been severely annoyed by a whole army of local fairies passing through the house at night. All in all, we can say with a certain amount of assurance that the faith in The Good People is still widely held to in rural Ireland. Indeed, I sometimes think it will die very hard; as when I hear a wealthy Dublin builder engaged in building himself a house in the suburbs sheepishly confessing in private to having "turned the sod" a few days before having the foundations dug. This "turning of the sod" involves cutting and turning over one sod at each angle of the proposed site a few days before the foundations are dug. The sods are left turned over to see if the fairies will show their disapproval of building there by turning the sods back at night; if, after a day or two, the four sods have been untouched, the men go ahead and dig the foundations, having got the all-clear from The Good People. Doubtless the council had neglected to take these wise precautions when building the cottage on the "fairy pass." In such ways an age-old belief follows the countryman into the city and makes the Irish townsman different from the townsman of the industrial age everywhere else. Wisps and scarves of poetry and folk-belief still cling around him. He is never far from their eternal wisdom and their timeless values.

In this handful of folktales, then, I have tried to give samples in English of authentic tales as spoken by Irish speakers with no change or doctoring of any kind, always keeping the translations as close as possible to their actual words. I have also included a few stories retold by Patrick Kennedy and collected by him from the English-speaking Irish countryman of the Pale, as the reader may like to compare them with those told in Gaelic by the Gaelic speakers of the South and West.

In my search and selection I have had the generous help and advice of many people, notably Dr. Delargy, Dr. Sean O'Sullivan and Dr. Wall of the Irish Folklore Commission, and Mr. Dermot Foley and the staff of the Irish Central Students' Library. To these I wish to express my warmest thanks and appreciation for their always willing help.

Contents

The
Fairy
Faith

The Fairy Host (The Slua Shee)

Wнo are the Slua Shee?

Sitting beside the fire on a cold, stormy night in winter, we love to listen to the terrifying and wondrous tales of their doings, even while we are trembling with fear at their telling. We draw a little closer to each other as the wind sweeps down from the hills in stormy gusts, and the wild waves break over the sunken rocks with a thunderous noise. As the storm and the tales go on the blood runs cold in our veins at the thought of being caught and carried away by them on our way home to our own houses.

Who are they, the Slua Shee? Many are the stories told of them, but for all that 'tis little we know of them and their ways. Some say they are the fallen angels, whom God, Glory be to Him, drove out of heaven for their pride. Some talk of them as The Good People. I do not know why they should be called The Good People, for I never heard of much good they ever did anyone, though it is certain they did harm to many a one.

They are on sea as well as on land, and some say they are even more numerous on the sea. They are said to raise storms that drown a lot of people, and at other times they say they make the ocean calm and smooth as a millpond. Sometimes on nights when the moon is full the fishermen see them boating. They often ask for a light for their pipes, and the fishermen give it to them, for if they refused, The Good People would take their

3

revenge sooner or later by sending sudden storms around the fishing boats to capsize them and drown all in them.

If some of the young people die, a beautiful baby, a gentle maiden, a handsome boy or a young mother of children, the old folks do not believe it to be a natural death but think that the Slua Shee have carried them off.

It is not only at night that a person is stolen away by the fairies, it is often done during the day, especially if the person happens to be in a lonely place, but the favorite times for stealing are the fall of dark, at cockcrow in the morning and at midday.

When a person is stolen by the Slua Shee they sometimes leave someone in his place, such as another fairy who is made to look exactly like the stolen person, or maybe they would leave something to look like a person, such as a bundle of heather, for they are able to give human shape to anything they please.

A beautiful young girl died some time ago, and as was the custom in those days, her mother and all her people were keening over her. This went on till a wise woman of the place, who had spent a time away with the Slua Shee and knew their ways, came to the mother of the girl and told her that the form of the dead girl lying on the bed was only a bundle of heather, and that the real girl was away with The Good People.

A stolen person can be got back from the fairies, but he must be rescued within a certain time — some say seven days. But if he eats any food given him in the fairy world he is lost forever to the Slua Shee, for he loses all memory of his life among humans.

There are three things necessary to get a person back from the fairies — the herb of the fairy *lios*,* a waxen taper and a black-hafted knife.

---

* *lios:* a fairy fort.

THE SLUA SHEE

A good long time ago a woman got up in the middle of the
night to make a churn. She had to go out to the well for water. It
seemed to her husband that she was a long time outside, and he
got impatient and went out to the well to see what was keeping
her. He found her stretched dead before him in front of the well.
Three days after that a wise woman came to the man and told
him that his wife sent her to tell him that she had not tasted a
bit of fairy food yet, and that if he would come that night to a
certain little stream, and wait till the dead of night, the Slua
Shee would be going past. She said she would be riding on the
last horse, and when his forelegs would be on the little bridge
over the stream, if he jumped up, caught her by the hand, pulled
her off the horse and kissed her three times, she would be free to
go home with him and that the fairies would never again have
any claim on her. Then she gave him some herbs of the *lios*
and told him the answers to any questions that might be put to
him by The Good People. But it was all in vain for he never
went to meet her.

Often and often I have heard of people being stolen back
from the fairies. If the generation now on the brink of the grave
is telling the truth there were many such alive during their youthful days.

Many a one often asks, "Where do the fairies dwell?" They
seem to have their dwellings in many kinds of places. Sometimes
we hear that their mansions and palaces are in the hearts of the
green, beautiful hills. Again we hear they make their abode in
dark, gloomy glens, where forever sleeps the shade of night,
and the solitude is seldom broken but by the bleating of the goat,
the scream of the eagle or the rough voice of the wintry wind.
But no matter where they dwell they delight in a clean plot of
grass beside the door of the fairy fort, so that they may be
basking in the sun and warming themselves.

There is nothing that moves them to anger more than that a human should build a house near them, or even across a pathway they are wont to take, and all kinds of misfortune falls on the luckless person who has dared to encroach on their territory in this way. It may be the sudden death of himself or of one of his family, or his cattle might sicken and pine away, or their yield would lessen.

It is well known that the fairies have good food in plenty — oaten and wheaten bread, rolls of sweet butter, barrels of fish, streams of new milk, yellow honey and beeswax in handfuls, mead in *meathers* (large cups), beer and whiskey in oceans; in short, every luxury the heart may desire.

They do not spend all their time eating and feasting, however; they enjoy sports and contests as well, also duels and wrestling matches, dancing on the level hilltops on moonlit nights, leaping and hurdling on the smooth plains and somersaulting down the slopes. Or they might go digging the ground, graffing (hoeing), mowing the meadows or boat racing on the lakes or rivers.

There was once a man working in one of the copper mines of Beara. He had a large family of young children, and only for his good hardworking wife he would not have been able to keep the roof over their heads at all, for money was scarce and hard to come by. It was drawing on to summer and he had a fine meadow that was ready for cutting, but as he was working all day it was at night he had to go at the mowing and do it as best he could in the half darkness.

One night he came home and he brought a noggin of whiskey with him. He put it on his head and drank it down without lifting the bottle once. He got his scythe. It was night then, but the moon was so bright and clear that it was nearly as lightsome as the broad noonday. He went into the field and began sharpening his scythe and began mowing, slowly at first till he

had a space opened for himself. He sharpened his scythe again
and started laying swathes of clover and mountain grass whis-
tling around him. He was working away like that for a while till
he happened to pause and look around him. Then he saw seven
mowers going through the field scything away at their best.

He started again and never stopped scything for fear that if he
did his helpers would stop likewise. When he used to have his
own "blow" cut he used to go seven "blows" in advance so as to
keep clear of his fellow mowers. It was not long, you may be
sure, till the eight had half the field cut. By that time the seven
fairy mowers were coming so near him that a fear came over
him in spite of himself, and the hair was standing up on his
head like the bristles of a wild pig. After a while the fear got the
better of him and he made for home, locked the door well after
him and went to sleep till morning.

The next day his wife went out to look at the work her husband
had done in the meadow the night before, but instead of the
whole meadow being mown, as he told her, it was only every
eighth "blow" was cut and the rest was standing.

The Good People marry and are given in marriage, and they
have wedding feasts and christening feasts. There was a man
one time going to the city of Cork with two firkins of butter
to sell. The darkness of night overtook him before he could
reach any house to ask shelter till the morning. As he was going along the road a stranger came up beside him and asked
him would he come with him and stand sponsor for a child
that was in the throes of death in a nearby cottage. As the man
was unknown to him he was not inclined to go with him, but
the thought of the child dying without baptism made him make
up his mind to go.

He tied his horse to a bush and followed the stranger over a
fence by the roadside, and he soon found himself entering a

beautiful mansion. About a year previous to that his only daughter had died giving birth to a child, and as he went into one of the chambers of the mansion he saw his daughter alive and well on the bed, and the child to be christened was hers. After the christening a person came up to him and asked him what gift he would give the baby, his own grandson. "The best milch cow I have in the stall," he said.

He went on his way to Cork and he returned home, after selling his two firkins of butter, and the news that his wife had before him was that the best milking cow had died during the night. But he had no reason to be sorry for her loss, for he prospered after that, and wind and stream and tide were with him from that day out.

The Good People have cattle of all sorts — cows, goats, sheep and horses — just like ourselves. It was often I heard tell of a person who passed by a *lios* as the fairies were churning, and it was often remarked that it is on a Sunday they mostly do their work.

If a cow or a horse dies at the time when anyone in the family is sick, that is taken to show that an attempt has been made by the fairies to steal the sick person, but having failed to do that, they took the cow or the horse instead.

It is certain that the old people used to have great fear of the Slua Shee, but like everything else that appertains to the old days in Erin, that fear is fast disappearing, it is going from us with the tongue that told of their mighty deeds, their power and their adventures in the beautiful, musical Gaelic of our forefathers.

Where Bill Keane Lit His Pipe

*T*HERE WAS a contractor and pump-sinker in Tipperary by the name of Morrissey. My brother used to work as a carpenter for him at times.

When I was a young lad I used to go in, in wintertime, with the donkey to bring him home from work. I'd sit down at Morrissey's alongside the fire, waiting till the tradesmen would come in.

There were two old men, Bill Keane and Dick Cook, used to come visiting there. They were butter-carters in their day. This night Bill Keane was saying to Cook:

"Do you remember, Dick," says he, "the night of the house in the bog?"

"Begor, I do," says Dick. "'Twas very strange."

Now Mrs. Morrissey pressed Bill to tell the yarn.

"The funny part of it," says Bill, "was — there was no house there at all in the bog — and there was.

"I and Cook here were going to Thurles one night, with two horseloads of butter. When we got to the bog of Ballymore, Cook says to me:

" 'We had a right to kindle our pipes back the road; there's no house now for the next five miles.'

" 'Ah! sure we must only do without our smoke so,' says I — there were no Lucifers in them days.

"We jogged along for a couple of miles more, and in from the road about fifty yards — in the bog — I thought I saw a rush-light in a window. 'Hould on, Dick,' says I, 'there's a house here and we'll light up.'

" 'There's no house there,' says Dick. 'I traveled this road night and day and I'll bet you there isn't a house for two more miles.'

" 'Wait there a minute,' says I, jumping down off the car, 'I'm blind if there isn't.'

"I crossed over the ditch and struck for the light in the window. 'Twas a nice little thatched house, with the door open. I said: 'God bless ye all,' but got no reply. There was a good fire of turf, and a man sitting on a boss with his elbows on his knees and his head on his two hands. I went to the fire and kindled my pipe and turned round to come out again. Then I saw that the house was divided with a kind of curtain partition. The curtain was but half drawn, and inside the curtain there was a bed, with a corpse of a man laid out. I went to the side of the bed and said a prayer for the dead man and left. Cook was outside in the yard. Cook wouldn't light his pipe there at all, and he couldn't be persuaded that there was a house there all the time — and still he was looking at it. I wanted him to come in — no, he wouldn't; and he pulled a big furze that was growing nearby and stuck it on the side of the road where the house was then.

" 'I bet you any money, when we're coming back with the daylight tomorrow, there'll be no house there.'

" 'Yerra, go way ou'r that,' says I, 'how could I light my pipe so?'

"We continued our journey, unloaded at Thurles, and coming back early the evening after, there was plenty daylight when we were passing the same spot. There was the furze standing on the ditch where Cook stuck it, but not the shadow of a house.

"But I lit my pipe there anyway," said Bill.

Did the Tailor Get
the Thread Yet?

*H*ERE IS a yarn for you about a man that came back from the dead. He was Dwyer of Bearna — that's below near Solohead.

The tailors formerly used always to work in the farmers' houses. The farmers' wives used to card and spin their own wool from their own sheep. The weavers of Tipperary used to weave it for them, and after that it would be ready for the tailor.

The tailor was a very busy man them times, and when he'd come the way there would always be plenty of work before him. The farmer's family would be waiting for him some time after he had promised to come.

This particular tailor worked at Dwyer's of Bearna. He worked very hard, for he had promised another that he would be with him the following week. He was finishing a suit of clothes for the young man of the house, and on Saturday evening he came off the table.

"There you are now!" said the tailor. "I've no thread to sew on the buttons, as anxious as you were to get your suit for Sunday."

"Hould on there a minute," said the young man. "Oola isn't so far away. I'll be there and back before very long, and I'll have plenty of thread for you."

He took his stick and left for Oola there and then.

Night fell and he never returned. His people got anxious about him when it got dark. They called some neighbors and searched along the shortcut to Oola. Early next morning they found his body alongside a double ditch. They brought home the corpse. It was waked and buried.

The young man himself that went for the thread said that when he crossed the ditch he saw two teams hurling,* and there were any amount of hurleys thrown along the touchline. He looked at the game for a while, being a good hurler himself. One man came with a hurley from one of the teams, and he says: "Join in the game!" Another came and told him not to mind but to go on his way. Dwyer for the sport of it took the hurley and made off after the ball.

He didn't think himself that he was five minutes playing when the match was over. Both teams left the field and went into a house nearby. Dwyer rested for a while inside, and then he saw a big crowd of men filing out the door. None of them invited him to go, so he remained where he was.

When they were all gone, a very old man came up to him. "If you want to go home," said the old man, "I can let you off now if you like." Dwyer was delighted for somebody to show him the way home, because the men were strange to him, and the house was strange.

When he came to his normal senses where he found himself was on the Hill of Derk. When he was near his own house he thought of his message, but he knew that something had come over him. He said to himself that he would go in and see if the tailor was inside.

* *hurling:* an Irish game played with a crooked stick, not unsimilar to modern hockey.

'Twas a summer's evening. All the family were eating their supper. When they saw the dead man coming back they screamed and left the house — everyone but the father.

Dwyer said quite cool: "Father, did the tailor get the thread yet?"

"Yerra, that's more than twelve months ago since your tailor was here. Didn't we wake you and bury you — an' what's troubling you that's bringing you back?"

He made it clear to his father that he knew of where he was, and all his friends and neighbors came to see him after his coming back. But the mystery was — how the body that was buried was the same man as him that came back to live for years after in Bearna.

The Vacant Cow Bail

Aт Shronell-beg there is a cow shed where cows are tied during the winter months. I strolled in there one day and remarked to the boy that was feeding the cows:

"Why is there no cow tied in the center bail?"

He said the fairies would rip her (that is, would loose her from the bail).

"When we came here first," said he, "there was a door there where that bail is now. We said it was waste, and that we'd close in the door and put a cow there. We done it, and the following morning the cow was ripped and driven out. We didn't mind at first; we thought it was a flaw in the chain. But finally we found out that no fastening would hold a cow during the night to that bail. So that's why the bail is vacant."

Ned Crowe, who is working at Condon's of Shronell, was the man that told me that.

Midnight Races

I REMEMBER well the night; it was the time of the hard spring weather. Some little snow had fallen in the beginning of the night — just enough to cover the ground. The night improved then and a light frost came on top of the snow. It was a moonlight night.

The horses were taken out of the houses that night (by the fairies) in Baile and Lios Cearna. The tracks of the horses were seen at the doors in the morning. When the people got up in the morning the hoofprints were there in the snow.

They had a race then from the old workhouse to the cemetery. There was a gap in the field behind the cemetery and the tracks were plain in and out — there and around the fields; I saw it myself and the whole world saw it. People heard them also. My father was on the road to Tralee that night and everyone was surprised that he had not seen them, but he had not. They went then westwards below Cill na nUghdaran, perhaps as far as Bun Conarach. There was a boy from this village below who used to be with them and he was with them that night. He said when they were going at full speed westwards a cow of Flaherty's of Lios Cearna was on the road before them and had given the horse and rider a fall, "but she will never again knock down anyone," said he.

He spoke the truth. The cow lay crippled near the fence next morning and died soon after.

The Magic Ship

*F*ISHING for mackerel we were in autumn; it is now more than forty years ago. It was a very fine night with no clouds to obscure the stars; it was in no wise dark. There were three of us — two of ourselves and another Murphy from the village, a son of the man called Uibh Rathac, he was a youth. It was past midnight, one or two o'clock, perhaps, and we had set the nets at the mouth of Cuas na Ceannaine, east of the Ceannan itself. The six nets were stretched westwards and out to sea and we were at the inner end. The three of us saw her together — a large ship in full sail. She lay between us and Mionan — about fifty spades (a hundred paces) away — like a jet-black tower (of cloud). She was not far from the cliff as the point of the Mionan ran further out than where we were. We were afraid, naturally, and said to each other that we had better haul the nets and run. Another man said to leave them, for we would be moving towards the ship in the hauling, which we did not wish to do. She was nearer the tail nets than the inboard ones. We did not know what to do and young Murphy was very much afraid. Another canoe had cast north of us, between us and Binn Point, and he was screaming and shouting at them: "You over there, come and help us," for he thought that the ship would pounce on us suddenly. The three of us were frightened enough. The ship was not moving, she was so high above us that you

would have to look upwards to see the tops of her sails. There
she was without a move, standing like a jet-black mass up out
of the water right to the top. She showed no light, neither did
we see anybody on board nor hear a sound or a word. She appeared very strange to us but our fear was abating when she
did not approach us. We left the nets set; there was no heavy
sea or current — there never is during neap tides. She remained there for a good half hour. She remained there as
long as that before she began at all to melt away. Then she
began to grow smaller, the top part disappearing first. She began growing smaller and smaller and smaller till she appeared
to be no bigger than a boat. She was no bigger than a canoe
just before she melted (vanished) altogether. We stayed out
till morning but I think we had no good catch. We met a couple of other canoes that had been fishing about the same place
and they told us they had not seen her at all.

The Sow Taken by the Fairies

ABOUT FIFTY years ago, there was a man passing a *rath** in Knocknaboley about two o'clock in the night looking for a sow. He saw a sow and nine boneens in the *rath*. So he went to hunt the sow back, but the sow wouldn't move, only grunt at him. Then a whole lot of little men came around him and they said:

"Leave that sow there! That's not your sow. That's our sow."

"You're a liar," he says to the fairies, "that's my sow!"

So one fellow said: "I'll give you one chance more, and if you don't go away the sow will eat you."

So the sow said to him: "Go away, good man!"

"It's time to go now," says he, "when the sow is speaking."

So he went home and another man was plowing in the field near the *rath* next day, and says the other man, Jack Byrne, to him:

"There is no such thing as fairies."

"There is," says he, "because I was looking for the sow the other night, and I seen a sow and nine boneens in the *rath*."

"Ah, go o' that, man, there's no such thing. If they don't leave bread and butter there for me I'll plow up the *rath*."

---

* *rath:* an early ramparted dwelling believed for many years by the country people to have been a dwelling of The Good People.

20

"Don't do any such thing. There is a *rath* there, and The Good People are in it."

So, begor, they came around, and in the *rath* there was a tablecloth spread out and bread and butter and cheeses and currant cake and every class there.

"Now," says he to Byrne, "will you ate it?"

But no, begor, they wouldn't ate it. They plowed around the field, and the horses began to kick, and Byrne got in between them, and he was killed.

One night after, this man was passing by the *rath* and he heard the grandest of music, and a voice said to him:

"Come in and have something to eat!"

"No, thank you, my good friend," he says, "I am going home for my stirabout."

"Oh, we have nicer than stirabout for you here."

But he wouldn't go in. So the voice said:

"I have good news for you. You are going to get a lot of money."

And he did. The next day he plowed up a box and it was full of sovereigns.

The Dance in Ballycumber

O NE NIGHT a young man was going to a dance in Ballycumber.
He was going through Rathcot for a shortcut when he heard the
loveliest of music and singing in the *rath,* which was all lit up.
He saw a girl there that had been taken by the fairies, and he
went in and danced with her and had a great time. The fairies
came to him with fruit and grapes and all kinds of eatables
and wanted him to take them, but she told him not to eat anything or he would be kept. She told him to go away and
not to look back until he had crossed the river. So he went, but
when he was halfway across he looked back and his head was
turned sideways, and was that way till the day of his death.

THE DANCE IN BALLYCOMBER

The Fairy Dinner

A MAN named Kenny went to dig Rathmeague *rath* for Mr. Willoughby of Moyne. When dinnertime came a girl brought him his dinner, and he ate it. Later on another girl came to him with another dinner, and he asked her where she was going with the two dinners. She said she was not there before. It was a fairy dinner he got first; he did not live long afterwards.

The Cardplayer and the Fairies

ONE NIGHT as a cardplayer from here was going home from a game he met another man who asked him to play a rubber. It was a moonlight night, so they sat down to play. When they were going to part a lot of men riding calves came up, and there was two calves with no riders. So he got up on one, and the stranger on the other, and off they went across hills and dales. When they were starting the stranger told him not to speak a word and he would leave him back home where he started. They galloped all night until they came to a big river, and the calf jumped the river so well that the man said: "Well lepped of a calf if I never got home!" With that he broke the spell, and they let him down, and he had to stop there till morning, and then he found himself outside Rathdrum, and he had to get home as best he could.

The Story of Nora Mackay
and The Fairies

THERE WAS a poor widow woman living in Castle Hacket, near Knockma in the County Galway, one time, and her name was Nora Mackay. She was a midwife by calling and she was very poor.

One snowy winter's day she was out gathering faggots to make a fire to warm the children, when all of a sudden she heard the noise of hammering behind her. She looked around, and there she saw a small young man dressed in a red coat, leather breeches and wearing an apron. He was tapping a piece of leather on an iron last that he had on his knees. It came to her mind on the spot that this must be the leprechaun, the fairy shoemaker, that she had heard so much about all her life, and how he would have to give you all his gold if you kept your eyes on him, without once looking away. She had often heard that if you once took your eyes off him, even for a second, he would disappear, and you would never see him again.

Nora made towards him, and if she did, didn't he jump up, and the piece of leather he was hammering fell to the ground.

"Pick that up," said he to her.

She bent down to pick up the leather, as he told her, and if she did, when she looked back again, he was gone clean out of her sight. She was very sad and sorrowful at losing him, and she said to herself: "I've lost my riches now, but there's no help for it; anyway God's help is nearer than the door."

Sadly she threw the bundle of faggots up on her back and made for home. As she was going along she saw a man riding a white horse coming towards her. He saluted her and said: "Do you know a woman around here called Nora Mackay?"

" 'Tis a fortunate meeting for us, sir," said Nora, "for I am the woman you are looking for."

"If you are," said the horseman, "jump up behind me on the horse."

He backed the horse up to a little mound. Nora threw the faggots off her back and stood up on the mound and jumped up on the horse behind the rider. He went off then as quickly as the horse could go. He told Nora that Nuala, queen of Finvara, King of the Fairies, was very sick when he left the palace. Nora knew then that the horseman was one of The Good People.

After a while he turned in through a long, dark porch under the hill. Nora grew very frightened as she was going through the darkness. Before long she saw a dwelling before her, the like of which, for beauty and grandeur, she had never set eyes on in her whole life.

The horseman rode up to the great door of the palace, and she was taken down from the horse. Standing at the door, before her, were twelve ladies-in-waiting. Each one of them gave Nora Mackay a hundred thousand welcomes, calling her by name.

"Long life to you," said Nora, "but how did you find out my name?"

"Never mind that now, Nora," said one of them.

Nora was taken upstairs then to the queen's bedroom, and they left her there alone with the queen. Nora wasn't long there till a young son was born to the queen. Everyone in the court was delighted to hear that news.

Nora did whatever was to be done for the queen, and then she dressed the child, and gave it back to the queen in bed. A young lady came in then, and the queen told her to take Nora out and give her something to eat. Nora was given food and drink, and never in her life before had she had such beautiful food.

She stayed a month with The Good People in the palace. All that time she thought she was in heaven itself, and she could not imagine how she was ever going to leave such a beautiful place.

As soon as the queen was up and better, she and her ladies-in-waiting went out one day. There was a little font inside the door of the palace. The queen dipped the tip of her finger into the font, and she rubbed it on her right eye, and all her ladies did likewise. She noticed that they used to do that every time they left the palace, so that they would be invisible to human creatures. When they had gone out, Nora said to herself: "If it is good for them, it is good for me," and she did what they had done, and rubbed the water on her right eye.

Shortly after that the queen paid Nora and told her she would not keep her any longer from her home and from her children. Then she asked Nora if she had a cow. "Indeed I have not, my love," said Nora.

"Here's ten pounds for you and buy a cow," said the queen. The cows were cheap at that time, so she told Nora to buy provisions with anything she had left after paying for the cow.

Nora said goodbye and left a blessing with the queen. She went to the fair of Turramore and bought a cow. She was going out of the fair when she saw twelve of the most beautiful women she had ever seen in her life, and the queen was at the head of them, coming towards her through the crowd. Nora asked her how the child was.

"He is very well," said the queen, "but with what eye did you see me?" she asked Nora.

"I saw you with this eye," said Nora, putting her hand on her right eye.

The queen blew a little puff of wind under the eye, and said to her: "Now you will never see me again."

Nora came home sadly. Setting out in the morning, that was not how she thought she would be coming back. She took a cow home with her, and if she did, it was a cow that had cost her a lot, for she had lost her right eye on account of her. Whatever money she had left after buying the cow, she took with her to Tuam and bought provisions with it. She lived a long time after that, blind of one eye, but never again did she see any of The Good People to the day of her death.

Fairy Cows

IN THE PARISH of Drummor lived a farmer whose name was Tom Connors. He had a nice bit of land and four cows. He was a fine, strong, honest man, and had a wife and five children.

Connors had one cow which was better than the other three, and she went by the name of Cooby. She got the name because her two horns turned in toward her eyes. They used to feed her often at the house, and she was very gentle, and had a heifer calf every year for five or six years.

On one corner of Connor's farm there was a fairy fort, and the cow Cooby used to go into the fort, but Connors always drove her out, and told his wife and the boys to keep her away from the fort, "For," said he, "it isn't much luck there is for any cow or calf that is fond of going into these fairy forts."

Soon they noticed that Cooby's milk was failing her and that she was beginning to pine away, and though she had the same food at home as before, nothing would do her but to go to the fort.

One morning when Connors went to drive his cows home to be milked he found Cooby on the field and her forelegs broken. He ran home that minute for a knife, killed and skinned the cow, made four parts of the carcass, put the pieces in a hamper, and carried the hamper home on his back.

What of the meat himself and family didn't eat fresh he salted, and now and then of a Sunday evening or a holiday they had a meal of it with cabbage, and it lasted a long time.

One morning after Tom was gone to the bog to cut turf the wife went out to milk, and what should she see but a cow walking into the fort, and she the living image of Cooby. Soon the cow came out, and with her a girl with a pail and spancel.

"Oh, then," said Mrs. Connors, "I'd swear that is Cooby, only that we are after eating the most of her. She has the white spots on her back and the horns growing into her eyes."

The girl milked the cow, and then cow and girl disappeared. Mrs. Connors meant to tell her husband that night about the cow, but she forgot it, they having no meat for supper.

The following day Tom went again to cut turf, the woman went to milk, and again she saw the cow go into the fort and the girl come out with a pail and a spancel. The girl tied the cow's legs, and sitting under her began to milk.

"God knows 'tis the very cow, and sure why shouldn't I know Cooby with the three white spots and the bent horns," thought Mrs. Connors, and she watched the cow and girl till the milking was over and thought, "I'll tell Tom tonight, and he may do what he likes, but I'll have nothing to do with fort or fairies myself."

When Connors came home in the evening, the first words before him were:

"Wisha then, Tom, I have the news for you tonight."

"And what news is it?" asked Tom.

"You remember Cooby?"

"Why shouldn't I remember Cooby, and we after eating the most of her?"

"Indeed then, Tom, I saw Cooby today, and she inside in the fort and a girl milking her."

"Don't be making a fool of yourself. Is it the cow we are eating that would be in the fort giving milk?"

"Faith, then, I saw her and the three white spots on her back."

"But what is the use in telling me the like of that," said Tom, "when we haven't but two or three bits of her left inside in the tub?"

"If we haven't itself, I saw Cooby today."

"Well, I'll go in the morning, and if it's our Cooby that's in it I'll bring her home with me," said Tom, "if all the devils in the fort were before me."

"Ah, Tom, if it's to the fort you'll be going, don't forget to put holy water over you before you go."

Early in the morning Tom started across his land and never stopped till he came to the fort, and there, sure enough, he saw the cow walking in through the gap to the fort, and he knew her that minute.

"'Tis my cow Cooby," said Connors, "and I'll have her. I'd like to see the man would keep her from me."

That minute the girl came out with her pail and spancel and was going up to Cooby.

"Stop where you are; don't milk that cow!" cried Connors, and springing toward the cow he caught her by the horn. "Let go the cow," said Tom; "this is my cow. It's a year that she's from me now. Go to your master and tell him to come out to me."

The girl went inside the fort and disappeared, but soon a fine-looking young man came and spoke to Connors.

"What are you doing here, my man," asked he, "and why did you stop my servant from milking the cow?"

"She is my cow," said Tom, "and by that same token I'll keep her; and that's why I stopped the girl from milking her."

"How could she be your cow? Haven't I this cow a long time, and aren't you after eating your own cow?"

"I don't care what cow I'm after eating," said Tom. "I'll have this cow, for she is my Cooby."

They argued and argued. Tom declared that he'd take the cow home. "And if you try to prevent me," said he to the man, "I'll tear the fort to pieces or take her with me."

"Indeed, then, you'll not tear the fort."

Tom got so vexed that he made at the man. The man ran and Tom after him into the fort. When Tom was inside he forgot all about fighting. He saw many people dancing and enjoying themselves, and he thought, "Why shouldn't I do the like myself?" With that he made up to a fine-looking girl, and, taking her out to dance, told the piper to strike up a hornpipe, and he did.

Tom danced till he was tired. He offered twopence to the piper, but not a penny would the piper take from him.

The young man came up and said: "Well, you are a brave man and courageous, and for the future we'll be good friends. You can take the cow."

"I will not take her; you may keep her and welcome, for you are all very good people."

"Well," said the young man, "the cow is yours, and it's why I took her because there were many children in the fort without nurses, but the children are reared now, and you may take the cow. I put an old stray horse in place of her and made him look like your own beast, and it's an old horse you're eating all the year. From this out you'll grow rich and have luck. We'll not trouble you, but help you."

Tom took the cow and drove her home. From that out Tom Connors's cows had two calves apiece and his mare had two

foals and his sheep two lambs every year, and every acre of
the land he had gave him as much crop in one year as another
man got from an acre in seven. At last Connors was a very rich
man; and why not, when the fairies were with him?

The Fairy Child

*T*HERE WAS a sailor that lived up in Grange when he was at home; and one time, when he was away seven or eight months, his wife was brought to bed of a fine boy. She expected her husband home soon, and she wished to put off the christening of the child till he'd be on the spot. She and her husband were not natives of the country, and they were not as much afraid of leaving the child unchristened as our people would be.

Well, the child grew and throve, and the neighbors all bothered the woman to take him to Father M.'s to be baptized, and all they said was no use. Her husband would be soon home, and then they'd have a joyful christening.

There happened to be no one sick up in that neighborhood for some time, so the priest did not come to the place, nor hear of the birth, and none of the people about her could make up their minds to tell upon her, it is such an ugly thing to be informing; and then the child was so healthy, and the father might be on the spot any moment.

So the time crept on, and the lad was a year and a half old, and his mother, up to that time, never lost five nights' rest by him; when one evening that she came in from binding after the reapers, she heard wonderful whingeing and lamenting from the little bed where he used to sleep. She ran over to him and asked him what ailed him.

"Oh, Mammy, I'm sick, and I'm hungry, and I'm cold; don't pull down the blanket."

Well, the poor woman ran and got some boiled bread and milk as soon as she could, and she asked her other son, that was about seven years old, when he took sick.

"Oh, Mother," says he, "he was as happy as a king, playing near the fire about two hours ago, and I was below in the room, when I heard a great rush, like as if a whole number of fowls were flying down the chimley. I heard my brother giving a great cry, and then another sound, like as if the fowls were flying out again, and when I got into the kitchen there he was, so miserable-looking that I hardly knew him, and he pulling his hair and his clothes, and his poor face so dirty. Take a look at him, and try do you know him at all."

So when she went to feed him she got such a fright, for his poor face was like an old man's, and his body, and legs, and arms, all thin and hairy. But still he resembled the child she left in the morning, and "Mammy, Mammy" was never out of his mouth. She heard of people being fairy-struck, so she supposed it was that that happened to him, but she never suspected her own child to be gone, and a fairy child left in its place.

Well, it's he that kept the poor woman awake many a night after, and never let her have a quiet day, crying for bread and milk, and mashed pitatytees, and stirabout; and it was still "Mammy, Mammy, Mammy," and the *glows* (noise) and the moans were never out of his mouth. Well, he had like to eat the poor woman out of house and home, and the very flesh off her bones with watching and sorrow. Still, nothing could persuade her that it wasn't her own child that was in it.

One neighbor and another neighbor told her their minds plain enough. "Now, ma'am, you see what it is to leave a child without being christened. If you done your duty, fairy, nor spirit,

THE FAIRY CHILD

nor divel, would have no power over your child. That *oun-kran* [cross creature] in the bed is no more your child nor I am, but a little imp that the *Duine Sighe* [fairy people] — God between us and harm! — left you. By this and by that, if you don't whip him up and come along with us to Father M.'s, we'll go, hotfoot, ourselves, and tell him all about it. Christened he must be before the world is a day older."

So she went over and soothered him, and said, "Come alanna, let me dress you, and we'll go and be christened."

And such roaring and screeching as came out of his throat would frighten the Danes.

"I haven't the heart," says she at last, "and sure if we attempted to take him in that state we'd have the people of the three townlands follying us to the priest's, and I'm afeard he'd take it very badly."

The next day when she came in, in the evening, she found him quite clean and fresh-looking, and his hair nicely combed.

"Ah, Pat," says she to her other son, "was it you that done this?"

Well, he said nothing till he and his mother were up at the fire, and the *angashore* (wretch) of a child in his bed in the room.

"Mother," says he then, in a whisper, "the neighbors are right, and you are wrong. I was out a little bit, and when I was coming round by the wall at the back of the room, I heard some sweet voices as if they were singing inside; and so I went to the crack in the corner, and what was round the bed but a whole parcel of nicely dressed little women, with green gowns; and they singing, and dressing the little fellow, and combing his hair, and he laughing and crowing with them. I watched for a long time, and then I stole round to the door, but the moment I pulled the string of the latch I hears the music changed to his whimpering and crying, and when I got into the room there was no sign of anything only himself. He was a little better-looking, but as cantankerous as ever."

"Ah," says the mother, "you are only joining the ill-natured neighbors; you're not telling a word of truth."

Next day Pat had a new story.

"Mother," says he, "I was sitting here while you were out, and I began to wonder why he was so quiet, so I went into the room to see if he was asleep. There he was, sitting up with his old face on him, and he frightened the life out of me, he spoke so plain. 'Paudh,' says he, 'go and light your mother's pipe, and let me have a shough; I'm tired o' my life lying here.' 'Ah, you thief,' says I, 'wait till you hear what she'll say to you when I tell her this.' 'Tell away, you pickthanks,' says he; 'she won't believe a word you say.' "

"And neither do I believe one word from you," said the mother.

At last a letter came from the father, that was serving on board the *Futhryom* (*Le Foudroyant?*), saying he'd be home after the letter as soon as coaches and ships could carry him.

"Now," says the poor woman, "we'll have the christening any-way."

So the next day she went to New Ross to buy sugar and tay, and beef and pork, to give a grand let-out to welcome her husband; but bedad the longheaded neighbors took that opportunity to gain their ends of the fairy imp. They gathered round the house, and one stout woman came up to the bed, promiskis-like, and wrapped him up in the quilt before he had time to defend himself, and away down the lane to the Boro she went, and the whole townland at her heels. He thought to get away, but she held him pinned as if he was in a vise; and he kept

roaring, and the crowd kept laughing, and they never crack-
cried till they were at the steppingstones going to Ballybawn
from Grange.

Well, when he felt himself near the water he roared like a
core (chorus) of bulls, and kicked like the divel, but my brave
woman wasn't to be daunted. She got on the first steppingstone,
and the water, as black as night from the turf *mull* (mould),
running under her. He felt as heavy as lead, but she held on to
the second. Well, she thought she'd go down there with the
roaring, and the weight, and the dismal color of the river, but
she got to the middle stone, and there down through the quilt
he fell as a heavy stone would through a muslin handkerchief.
Off he went, whirling round and round, and letting the fright-
fulest laughs out of him, and showing his teeth and cracking his
fingers at the people on the banks.

"Oh, yous think yous are very clever, now," says he. "You
may tell that fool of a woman from me that all I'm sorry for is
that I didn't choke her, or do worse for her, before her husband
comes home; bad luck to yous all!"

Well, they all came back joyful enough, though they were a
little frightened. But weren't they rejoiced to meet the poor
woman running to them with her fine healthy child in her
arms, that she found in a delightful sleep when she got back
from the town. You may be sure the next day didn't pass over
him till he was baptized, and the next day his father got
safe home. Well, I needn't say how happy they were; but bedad the woman was a little ashamed of herself next Sunday at
Rathnure Chapel while Father James was preaching about the
wickedness of neglecting to get young babies baptized as soon as
possible after they're born.

The Fairy Nurse

*T*HERE WAS once a little farmer and his wife living near Coolgarrow. They had three children, and my story happened while the youngest was on the breast. The wife was a good wife enough, but her mind was all on her family and her farm, and she hardly ever went to her knees without falling asleep, and she thought the time spent in the chapel was twice as long as it need be. So, begonies, she let her man and her two children go before her one day to Mass, while she called to consult a fairy-man about a disorder one of her cows had. She was late at the chapel, and was sorry all the day after, for her husband was in grief about it, and she was very fond of him.

Late that night he was wakened up by the cries of his children calling out, "Mother, Mother!" When he sat up and rubbed his eyes, there was no wife by his side, and when he asked the little ones what was become of their mother, they said they saw the room full of nice little men and women, dressed in white, and red, and green, and their mother in the middle of them, going out by the door as if she was walking in her sleep. Out he ran, and searched everywhere round the house, but neither tale nor tidings did he get of her for many a day.

Well, the poor man was miserable enough, for he was as fond of his woman as she was of him. It used to bring the salt tears down his cheeks to see his poor children neglected and dirty, as they often were, and they'd be bad enough only for a kind neighbor that used to look in whenever she could spare time. The infant was out with a wetnurse.

About six weeks after — just as he was going out to his work one morning — a neighbor, that used to mind women at their lying-in, came up to him, and kept step by step with him to the field, and this is what she told him:

"Just as I was falling asleep last night, I hears a horse's tramp in the *bawn* [lawn], and a knock at the door, and there, when I came out, was a fine-looking dark man, mounted on a black horse, and he told me to get ready in all haste, for a lady was in great want of me. As soon as I put on my cloak and things, he took me by the hand, and I was sitting behind him before I felt myself stirring.

" 'Where are we going, sir?' says I.

" 'You'll soon know,' says he; and he drew his fingers across my eyes, and not a *stim* [glimmer] remained in them. I kept a tight grip of him, and the dickens a know I knew whether he was going backwards or forwards, or how long we were about it, till my hand was taken again and I felt the ground under me. The fingers went the other way across my eyes, and there we were before a castle door, and in we went through a big hall and great rooms all painted in fine green colors, with red and gold bands and ornaments, and the finest carpets and chairs and tables and window curtains, and fine ladies and gentlemen walking about. At last we came to a bedroom with a beautiful lady in bed, and there he left me with her; and, bedad, it was not long till a fine bouncing boy came into the world. The lady clapped her hands and in came *Fir Dhorocha** [Dark Man], and kissed her and his son, and praised me, and gave me a bottle of green ointment to rub the child all over.

* Correctly, *Fear Doirche.*

"Well, the child I rubbed, sure enough; but my right eye began to smart me, and I put up my finger and gave it a rub, and
purshuin [misfortune] to me if ever I was so frightened. The
beautiful room was a big rough cave, with water oozing over
the edges of the stones and through the clay; and the lady, and
the lord, and the child, weazened, poverty-bitten crathurs —
nothing but skin and bone, and the rich dresses were old rags. I
didn't let on that I found any difference, and after a bit says
Fir Dhorocha:

" 'Go before me to the hall door, and I will be with you in a
few moments, and see you safe home.'

"Well, just as I turned into the outside cave, who should
I see watching near the door but poor Molly. She looked round
all frightened, and says she to me in a whisper:

" 'I'm brought here to give suck to the child of the king and
queen of the fairies; but there is one chance of saving me. All
the court will pass the cross near Templeshambo next Friday
night on a visit to the fairies of Old Ross. If John can catch me
by hand or cloak when I ride by, and has courage not to let go
his grip, I'll be safe. Here's the king. Don't open your mouth
to answer. I saw what happened with the ointment.'

"*Fir Dhorocha* didn't once cast his eye towards Molly, and
he seemed to have no suspicion of me. When we came out I
looked about me, and where do you think we were but in the
dyke of the Rath of Cromogue. I was on the horse again, which
was nothing but a big *boolian bui* [ragweed], and I was in dread
every minute I'd fall off; but nothing happened till I found myself in my own bawn. The king slipped five guineas into my
hand as soon as I was on the ground, and thanked me, and bade
me good night. I hope I'll never see his face again. I got into
bed, and couldn't sleep for a long time; and when I examined
my five guineas this morning, that I left in the table drawer the

last thing, I found five withered leaves of oak — bad *scran* [luck] to the giver!"

Well, you may all think on the fright, and the joy, and the grief the poor man was in when the woman finished her story. They talked, and they talked, but we needn't mind what they said till Friday night came, when both were standing where the mountain road crosses the one going to Ross.

There they stood looking towards the bridge of Thuar, and I won't keep you waiting, as they were in the dead of the night, with a little moonlight shining from over Kilachdiarmid. At last she gave a start, and "By this and by that," says she, "here they come, bridles jingling and feathers tossing." He looked, but could see nothing; and she stood trembling, and her eyes wide open, looking down the way to the ford of Ballinacolla.

"I see your wife," says she, "riding on the outside just so as to rub against us. We'll walk on promiskis-like, as if we suspected nothing, and when we are passing I'll give you a shove. If you don't do *your* duty then, dickens cure you!"

Well, they walked on easy, and the poor hearts beating in both their breasts; and though he could see nothing, he heard a faint jingle, and tramping, and rustling, and at last he got the push that she promised. He spread out his arms, and there was his wife's waist within them, and he could see her plain, but such a hullabaloo rose as if there was an earthquake; and he found himself surrounded by horrible-looking things, roaring at him, and striving to pull his wife away. But he made the sign of the cross, and bid them begone in God's name, and held his wife as if it was iron his arms were made of. Bedad, in one moment everything was as silent as the grave, and the poor woman lying in a faint in the arms of her husband and her good neighbor.

Well, all in good time she was minding her family and

her business again, and I'll go bail, after the fright she got, she spent more time on her knees, and avoided fairy-men all the days of the week, and particularly Sunday.

It is hard to have anything to do with The Good People without getting a mark from them. My brave midwife didn't escape no more nor another. She was one Thursday at the market of Enniscorthy, when what did she see walking among the tubs of butter but *Fir Dhorocha,* very hungry-looking, and taking a scoop out of one tub and out of another.

"Oh, sir," says she, very foolish, "I hope your lady is well, and the young heir."

"Pretty well, thank you," says he, rather frightened-like. "How do I look in this new suit?" says he, getting to one side of her.

"I can't see you plain at all, sir," says she.

"Well, now," says he, getting round her back to the other side.

"Musha, indeed sir, your coat looks no better nor a withered dock leaf."

"Maybe, then," says he, "it will be different now," and he struck the eye next him with a switch.

Begonies, she never saw a *stim* after with that one till the day of her death.

The Kildare Lurikeen

A YOUNG GIRL that lived in sight of Castle Carberry, near Edenderry, was going for a pitcher of water to the neighboring well one summer morning, when whom should she see sitting in a sheltery nook under an old thorn but the Lurikeen, working like vengeance at a little old brogue only fit for the foot of a fairy like himself. There he was, boring his holes, and jerking his waxed ends, with his little three-cornered hat with gold lace, his knee-breeches, his jug of beer by his side, and his pipe in his mouth. He was so busy at his work, and so taken up with an old ballad he was singing in Irish, that he did not mind Breedheen till she had him by the scruff o' the neck, as if he was in a vise.

"Ah, what are you doin'?" says he, turning his head round as well as he could. "Dear, dear! To think of such a purty colleen ketchin' a body, as if he was afther robbin' a hen roost! What did I do to be thrated in such an undecent manner? The very vulgarest young ruffin in the townland could do no worse. Come, come, Miss Bridget, take your hands off, sit down, and let us have a chat, like two respectable people."

"Ah, Mr. Lurikeen, I don't care a wisp of *borrach* [coarse tow] for your politeness. It's your money I want, and I won't take hand or eye from you till you put me in possession of a fine lob of it."

46

"Money indeed! Ah! where would a poor cobbler like me get it? Anyhow, there's no money hereabouts, and if you'll only let go my arms, I'll turn my pockets inside out, and open the drawer of my seat, and give you leave to keep every halfpenny you'll find."

"That won't do; my eyes'll keep going through you like darning needles till I have the gold. Begonies, if you don't make haste, I'll carry you, head and pluck, into the village, and there you'll have thirty pair of eyes on you instead of one."

"Well, well! Was ever a poor cobbler so circumvented! And if it was an ignorant, ugly *bosthoon* [fool] that done it, I would not wonder; but a decent, comely girl, that can read her *Poor Man's Manual* at the chapel, and . . ."

"You may throw your compliments on the stream there; they won't do for me, I tell you. The gold, the gold, the gold! Don't take up my time with your blarney."

"Well, if there's any to be got, it's undher the ould castle it is; we must have a walk for it. Just put me down, and we'll get on."

"Put you down indeed! I know a trick worth two of that; I'll carry you."

"Well, how suspicious we are! Do you see the castle from this?"

Bridget was about turning her eyes from the little man to where she knew the castle stood, but she bethought herself in time.

They went up a little hillside, and the Lurikeen was quite reconciled, and laughed and joked; but just as they got to the brow, he looked up over the ditch, gave a great screech, and shouted just as if a bugle horn was blew at her ears:

"Oh, murdher! Castle Carberry is afire."

Poor Biddy gave a great start and looked up towards the castle.

Paudyeen O'Kelly and the Weasel

A LONG TIME ago there was once a man of the name of Paudyeen O'Kelly living near Tuam in the County Galway. He rose up one morning early, and he did not know what time of day it was, for there was fine light coming from the moon. He wanted to go to the fair of Cauher-na-mart to sell a *sturk** of an ass that he had.

He had not gone more than three miles of the road when a great darkness came on, and a shower began falling. He saw a large house among trees about five hundred yards in from the road, and he said to himself that he would go to that house till the shower would be over. When he got to the house he found the door open before him, and in with him. He saw a large room to his left, and a fine fire in the grate. He sat down on a stool that was beside the wall, and began falling asleep, when he saw a big weasel coming to the fire with something yellow in its mouth, which it dropped on the hearthstone, and then it went away. She soon came back again with the same thing in her mouth, and he saw that it was a guinea she had. She dropped it on the hearthstone, and went away again. She was coming and going, until there was a great heap of guineas on the hearth. But at last, when he got her gone, Paudyeen

* *sturk:* a thick-set animal.

49

rose up, thrust all the gold she had gathered into his pockets, and out with him.

He was not gone far till he heard the weasel coming after him, and she screeching as loud as a bagpipes. She went before Paudyeen and got on the road, and she was twisting herself back and forwards, and trying to get a hold of his throat. Paudyeen had a good oak stick, and he kept her from him, until two men came up who were going to the same fair, and one of them had a good dog, and it routed the weasel into a hole in the wall.

Paudyeen went to the fair, and instead of coming home with the money he got for his old ass, as he thought would be the way with him in the morning, he went and bought a horse with some of the money he took from the weasel, and he came home and he riding. When he came to the place where the dog had routed the weasel into the hole in the wall, she came out before him, gave a leap up and caught the horse by the throat. The horse made off, and Paudyeen could not stop him, till at last he gave a leap into a big drain that was full up of water and black mud, and he was drowning and choking as fast as he could, until men who were coming from Galway came up and banished the weasel.

Paudyeen brought the horse home with him, and put him into the cow's byre and fell asleep.

Next morning, the day on the morrow, Paudyeen rose up early and went out to give his horse hay and oats. When he got to the door he saw the weasel coming out of the byre and she covered with blood.

"My seven thousand curses on you," said Paudyeen, "but I'm afraid you've harm done."

He went in and found the horse, a pair of milch cows, and two calves dead. He came out and set a dog he had after the weasel. The dog got a hold of her, and she got a hold of the dog. The dog was a good one, but he was forced to loose his hold of her before Paudyeen could come up. He kept his eye on her, however, all through, until he saw her creeping into a little hovel that was on the brink of a lake. Paudyeen came running, and when he got to the little hut he gave the dog a shake to rouse him and put anger on him, and then he sent him in before himself. When the dog went in he began barking. Paudyeen went in after him, and saw a *cailleach* (an old hag) in the corner. He asked her if she saw a weasel coming in there.

"I did not," said she. "I'm all destroyed with a plague of sickness, and if you don't go out quick you'll catch it from me."

While Paudyeen and the hag were talking the dog kept moving in all the time, till at last he gave a leap up and caught the hag by the throat. She screeched, and said:

"Paddy Kelly, take off your dog and I'll make you a rich man."

Paudyeen made the dog loose his hold, and said: "Tell me who are you, or why did you kill my horse and my cows?"

"And why did you bring away my gold that I was for five hundred years gathering throughout the hills and hollows of the world?"

"I thought you were a weasel," said Paudyeen, "or I wouldn't touch your gold; and another thing," says he, "if you're for five hundred years in this world, it's time for you to go to rest now."

"I committed a great crime in my youth," said the hag, "and now I am to be released from my sufferings if you can pay twenty pounds for a hundred and three score Masses for me."

"Where's the money?" says Paudyeen.

"Go and dig under a bush that's over a little well in the corner of that field there without, and you'll get a pot filled with gold. Pay the twenty pounds for the Masses, and yourself shall have the rest. When you'll lift the flag off the pot, you'll see a big black dog coming out, but don't be afraid before him; he is a son of mine. When you get the gold, buy the house in which you saw me at first. You'll get it cheap, for it has the name of there being a ghost in it. My son will be down in the cellar. He'll do you no harm, but he'll be a good friend to you. I shall be dead a month from this day, and when you get me dead put a coal under this little hut and burn it. Don't tell a living soul anything about me — and the luck will be on you."

"What is your name?" said Paudyeen.

"Maurya nee Keerwaun [Mary Kerwan]," said the hag.

Paudyeen went home, and when the darkness of the night came on he took with him a *loy* (spade), and went to the bush that was in the corner of the field, and began digging. It was not long till he found the pot, and when he took the flag off it a big black dog leaped out, and off and away with him, and Paudyeen's dog after him.

Paudyeen brought home the gold, and hid it in the cowhouse. About a month after that he went to the fair of Galway and bought a pair of cows, a horse, and a dozen sheep. The neighbors did not know where he was getting all the money; they said that he had a share with The Good People.

One day Paudyeen dressed himself and went to the gentleman who owned the large house where he first saw the weasel, and asked to buy the house of him, and the land that was round about.

"You can have the house without paying any rent at all; but there is a ghost in it, and I wouldn't like you to go to live in it without my telling you, but I couldn't part with the land without getting a hundred pounds more than you have to offer me."

"Perhaps I have as much as you have yourself," said Paudyeen. "I'll be here tomorrow with the money, if you're ready to give me possession."

"I'll be ready," said the gentleman.

Paudyeen went home and told his wife that he had bought a large house and a holding of land.

"Where did you get the money?" says the wife.

"Isn't it all one to you where I got it?" says Paudyeen.

The day on the morrow Paudyeen went to the gentleman, gave him the money, and got possession of the house and land; and the gentleman left him the furniture and everything that was in the house, in with the bargain.

Paudyeen remained in the house that night, and when darkness came he went down to the cellar, and he saw a little man with his two legs spread on a barrel.

"God save you, honest man," says he to Paudyeen.

"The same to you," says Paudyeen.

"Don't be afraid of me at all," says the little man. "I'll be a friend to you, if you are able to keep a secret."

"I am able, indeed; I kept your mother's secret, and I'll keep yours as well."

"Maybe you're thirsty?" says the little man.

"I'm not free from it," says Paudyeen.

The little man put a hand in his bosom and drew out a gold goblet. He gave it to Paudyeen, and said: "Draw wine out of that barrel under me."

Paudyeen drew the full up of the goblet, and handed it to the little man. "Drink yourself first," says he. Paudyeen drank, drew another goblet, and handed it to the little man, and he drank it.

"Fill up and drink again," said the little man. "I have a mind to be merry tonight."

The pair of them sat there drinking until they were half drunk. Then the little man gave a leap down to the floor, and said to Paudyeen: "Don't you like music?"

"I do, surely," says Paudyeen, "and I'm a good dancer, too."

"Lift up the big flag over there in the corner, and you'll get my pipes under it."

Paudyeen lifted the flag, got the pipes, and gave them to the little man. He squeezed the pipes on him and began playing melodious music. Paudyeen began dancing till he was tired. Then they had another drink, and the little man said:

"Do as my mother told you, and I'll show you great riches. You can bring your wife in here, but don't tell her that I'm there, and she won't see me. Any time at all that ale or wine are wanting, come here and draw. Farewell now; go to sleep, and come again to me tomorrow night."

Paudyeen went to bed, and it wasn't long till he fell asleep.

On the morning of the day on the morrow, Paudyeen went home and brought his wife and children to the big house, and they were comfortable. That night Paudyeen went down to the cellar; the little man welcomed him and asked him did he wish to dance?

"Not till I get a drink," said Paudyeen.

"Drink your 'nough," said the little man. "That barrel will never be empty as long as you live."

Paudyeen drank the full of the goblet, and gave a drink to the little man. Then the little man said to him:

"I am going to Doon-na-shee [the fortress of the fairies] to-night to play music for The Good People, and if you come with me you'll see fine fun. I'll give you a horse that you never saw the like of him before."

"I'll go with you, and welcome," said Paudyeen, "but what excuse will I make to my wife?"

"I'll bring you away from her side without her knowing it when you are both asleep together, and I'll bring you back to her the same way," said the little man.

"I'm obedient," says Paudyeen; "we'll have another drink before I leave you."

He drank drink after drink, till he was half drunk, and he went to bed with his wife.

When he awoke he found himself riding on a besom near Doon-na-shee, and the little man riding on another besom by his side. When they came as far as the green hill of the Doon, the little man said a couple of words that Paudyeen did not understand. The green hill opened, and the pair went into a fine chamber.

Paudyeen never saw before a gathering like that which was in the Doon. The whole place was full up of little people, men and women, young and old. They all welcomed little Donal — that was the name of the piper — and Paudyeen O'Kelly. The king and queen of the fairies came up to them, and said:

"We are all going on a visit tonight to Cnoc Matha, to the high king and queen of our people."

They all rose up then and went out. There were horses ready for each one of them and the *coash-t'ya bower** for the king and queen. The king and queen got into the coach, each man leaped on his own horse, and be certain that Paudyeen was not behind. The piper went out before them and began playing them music, and then off and away with them. It was not long till they came to Cnoc Matha. The hill opened and the king of the fairy host passed in.

Finvara and Nuala were there, the arch-king and queen of the fairy host of Connacht, and thousands of little persons. Finvara came up and said:

"We are going to play a hurling match tonight against the

---

* *coash-t'ya bower*: the headless coach (a spectral vision that goes through the country at night, and riders and drivers are all headless).

fairy host of Munster, and unless we beat them our fame is gone forever. The match is to be fought out on Moytura, under Slieve Belgadaun."

The Connacht host cried out: "We are all ready, and we have no doubt but we'll beat them."

"Out with ye all," cried the high king; "the men of the hill of Nephin will be on the ground before us."

They all went out, and little Donal and twelve pipers more before them, playing melodious music. When they came to Moytura, the fairy host of Munster and the fairy-men of the hill of Nephin were there before them. Now, it is necessary for the fairy host to have two live men beside them when they are fighting or at a hurling match, and that was the reason that little Donal took Paddy O'Kelly with him. There was a man they called the *yellow stongirya,** with the fairy host of Munster, from Ennis, in the County Clare.

It was not long till the two hosts took sides; the ball was thrown up between them, and the fun began in earnest. They were hurling away, and the pipers playing music, until Paudyeen O'Kelly saw the host of Munster getting the strong hand, and he began helping the fairy host of Connacht. The *stongirya* came up and he made at Paudyeen O'Kelly, but Paudyeen turned him head over heels. From hurling the two hosts began at fighting, but it was not long until the host of Connacht beat the other host. Then the host of Munster made flying beetles of themselves, and they began eating every green thing that they came up to. They were destroying the country before them until they came as far as Cong. Then there rose up thousands of doves out of the hole, and they swallowed down the beetles. That hole has no other name until this day but Pull-na-gullam, the dove's hole.

* *stongirya:* a sulky fellow.

When the fairy host of Connacht won their battle, they came back to Cnoc Matha joyous enough, and the King Finvara gave Paudyeen a purse of gold, and the little piper brought him home, and put him into bed beside his wife, and left him sleeping there.

A month went by after that without anything worth mentioning, until one night Paudyeen went down to the cellar, and the little man said to him:

"My mother is dead; burn the house over her."

"It is true for you," said Paudyeen. "She told me that she hadn't but a month to be on the world, and the month was up yesterday."

On the morning of the next day Paudyeen went to the hut and he found the hag dead. He put a coal under the hut and burned it. He came home and told the little man that the hut was burnt. The little man gave him a purse and said to him:

"This purse will never be empty as long as you are alive. Now, you will never see me more; but have a loving remembrance of the weasel. She was the beginning and the prime cause of your riches."

Then he went away and Paudyeen never saw him again.

Paudyeen O'Kelly and his wife lived for years after this in the large house, and when he died he left great wealth behind him, and a large family to spend it.

There now is the story for you, from the first word to the last, as I heard it from my grandmother.

The Legend of Bottle Hill

*I*T WAS in the good days when the little people, most impudently called fairies, were more frequently seen than they are in these unbelieving times, that a farmer, named Mick Purcell, rented a few acres of barren ground in the neighborhood of the once celebrated preceptory of Mourne, situated about three miles from Mallow, and thirteen from the "beautiful city called Cork." Mick had a wife and family. They all did what they could, and that was but little, for the poor man had no child grown up big enough to help him in his work; and all the poor woman could do was to mind the children, and to milk the one cow, and to boil the potatoes, and carry the eggs to market to Mallow; but with all they could do, 'twas hard enough on them to pay the rent. Well, they did manage it for a good while; but at last came a bad year, and the little grain of oats was all spoiled, and the chickens died of the pip, and the pig got the measles — she was sold in Mallow and brought almost nothing — and poor Mick found that he hadn't enough to half pay his rent, and two *gales**
were due.

"Why, then, Molly," says he, "what'll we do?"

"Wisha, then, mavourneen, what would you do but take the cow to the fair of Cork and sell her?" says she. "And Monday is

* *gale:* a periodical payment of rent.

58

fair day, and so you must go tomorrow, that the poor beast may be rested again the fair."

"And what'll we do when she's gone?" says Mick, sorrowfully.

"Never a know I know, Mick; but sure God won't leave us without Him, Mick; and you know how good He was to us when poor little Billy was sick, and we had nothing at all for him to take — that good doctor gentleman at Ballydahin come riding and asking for a drink of milk; and how he gave us two shillings; and how he sent the things and bottles for the child, and gave me my breakfast when I went over to ask him a question, so he did; and how he came to see Billy, and never left off his goodness till he was quite well?"

"Oh! You are always that way, Molly, and I believe you are right after all, so I won't be sorry for selling the cow; but I'll go tomorrow, and you must put a needle and thread through my coat, for you know 'tis ripped under the arm."

Molly told him he should have everything right; and about twelve o'clock next day he left her, getting a charge not to sell his cow except for the highest penny. Mick promised to mind it, and went his way along the road. He drove his cow slowly through the little stream which crosses it and runs under the old walls of Mourne. As he passed he glanced his eye upon the towers and one of the old elder trees, which were then only little bits of switches.

"Oh, then, if I only had half of the money that's buried in you, 'tisn't driving this poor cow I'd be now! Why, then, isn't it too bad that it should be there covered over with earth, and many a one besides me wanting? Well, if it's God's will, I'll have some money myself coming back."

So saying he moved on after his beast. 'Twas a fine day, and the sun shone brightly on the walls of the old abbey as he passed under them. He then crossed an extensive mountain tract, and after six long miles he came to the top of that hill — Bottle Hill 'tis called now, but that was not the name of it then, and just there a man overtook him.

"Good morrow," says he. "Good morrow, kindly," says Mick, looking at the stranger, who was a little man, you'd almost call him a dwarf, only he wasn't quite so little neither; he had a bit of an old wrinkled, yellow face, for all the world like a dried cauliflower, only he had a sharp little nose, and red eyes, and white hair, and his lips were not red, but all his face was one color, and his eyes were never quiet, but looking at everything, and although they were red they made Mick feel quite cold when he looked at them. In truth, he did not much like the little man's company; and he couldn't see one bit of his legs nor his body, for though the day was warm, he was all wrapped up in a big greatcoat.

Mick drove his cow something faster, but the little man kept up with him. Mick didn't know how he walked, for he was almost afraid to look at him, and to cross himself, for fear the old man would be angry. Yet he thought his fellow traveler did not seem to walk like other men, nor to put one foot before the other, but to glide over the rough road — and rough enough it was — like a shadow, without noise and effort. Mick's heart trembled within him, and he said a prayer to himself, wishing he hadn't come out that day, or that he was on Fair Hill, or that he hadn't the cow to mind, that he might run away from the bad thing — when, in the midst of his fears, he was again addressed by his companion.

"Where are you going with the cow, honest man?"

"To the fair of Cork, then," says Mick, trembling at the shrill and piercing tones of the voice.

"Are you going to sell her?" said the stranger.

"Why, then, what else am I going for but to sell her?"

"Will you sell her to me?"

Mick started — he was afraid to have anything to do with the little man, and he was more afraid to say no.

"What'll you give for her?" at last says he.

"I'll tell you what, I'll give you this bottle," says the little one, pulling the bottle from under his coat.

Mick looked at him and the bottle, and, in spite of his terror, he could not help bursting into a loud fit of laughter.

"Laugh if you will," said the little man, "but I tell you this bottle is better for you than all the money you will get for the cow in Cork — ay, than ten thousand times as much."

Mick laughed again.

"Why, then," says he, "do you think I am such a fool as to give my good cow for a bottle — and an empty one, too? Indeed, then, I won't."

"You had better give me the cow, and take the bottle — you'll not be sorry for it."

"Why then, and what would Molly say? I'd never hear the end of it; and how would I pay the rent? And what should we do without a penny of money?"

"I tell you this bottle is better to you than money — take it, and give me the cow. I ask you for the last time, Mick Purcell."

Mick started. "How does he know my name?" thought he.

The stranger proceeded: "Mick Purcell, I know you, and I have regard for you; therefore, do as I warn you, or you may be sorry for it. How do you know but your cow will die before you go to Cork?"

Mick was going to say "God forbid!" but the little man went on (and he was too attentive to say anything to stop him; for

Mick was a civil man, and he knew better than to interrupt a gentleman, and that's what many people, that hold their heads higher, don't mind now).

"And how do you know but there will be much cattle at the fair, and you will get a bad price, or maybe you might be robbed when you are coming home; but what need I talk more to you when you are determined to throw away your luck, Mick Purcell."

"Oh, no, I would not throw away my luck, sir," said Mick; "and if I was sure the bottle was as good as you say, though I never liked an empty bottle, although I had drank the contents of it, I'd give you the cow in the name —"

"Never mind names," said the stranger, "but give me the cow; I would not tell you a lie. Here, take the bottle, and when you go home do what I direct exactly."

Mick hesitated.

"Well, then, goodbye, I can stay no longer; once more, take it, and be rich; refuse it, and beg for your life, and see your children in poverty, and your wife dying for want — that will happen to you, Mick Purcell!" said the little man with a malicious grin, which made him look ten times more ugly than ever.

"Maybe 'tis true," said Mick, still hesitating: he did not know what to do — he could hardly help believing the old man — and at length, in a fit of desperation, he seized the bottle.

"Take the cow," said he, "and if you are telling a lie, the curse of the poor will be on you."

"I care neither for your curses nor your blessings, but I have spoken truth, Mick Purcell, and that you will find tonight, if you do what I tell you."

"And what's that?" says Mick.

"When you go home, never mind if your wife is angry, but be quiet yourself, and make her sweep the room clean, set the table

out right, and spread a clean cloth over it; then put the bottle on
the ground, saying these words: 'Bottle, do your duty,' and you
will see the end of it."

"And is this all?" says Mick.

"No more," said the stranger. "Goodbye, Mick Purcell — you
are a rich man."

"God grant it!" said Mick, as the old man moved after the
cow, and Mick retraced the road towards his cabin; but he
could not help turning back his head to look after the purchaser
of his cow, who was nowhere to be seen.

"Lord between us and harm!" said Mick. "He can't belong to
this earth; but where is the cow?" She too was gone, and Mick
went homeward muttering prayers and holding fast the bottle.

"And what would I do if it broke?" thought he. "Oh! But
I'll take care of that." So he put it into his bosom, and went on
anxious to prove his bottle, and doubting of the reception he
should meet from his wife. Balancing his anxieties with his ex-
pectations, his fears with his hopes, he reached home in the evening, and surprised his wife, sitting over the turf fire in the big
chimney.

"Oh! Mick, are you come back? Sure you weren't at Cork all
the way! What has happened to you? Where is the cow? Did
you sell her? How much money did you get for her? What
news have you? Tell us everything about it."

"Why, then, Molly, if you'll give me time, I'll tell you all
about it. If you want to know where the cow is, 'tisn't Mick can
tell you, for the never a know does he know, where she is now."

"Oh! Then you sold her; and where's the money?"

"Arrah! Stop awhile, Molly, and I'll tell you all about it."

"But what is that bottle under your waistcoat?" said Molly,
spying its neck sticking out.

"Why, then, be easy now, can't you?" says Mick, "till I tell it to you," and putting the bottle on the table — "That's all I got for the cow."

His poor wife was thunderstruck. "All you got! And what good is that, Mick? Oh! I never thought you were such a fool; and what'll we do for the rent? And what —"

"Now, Molly," says Mick, "can't you hearken to reason? Didn't I tell you how the old man, or whatsomever he was, met me — no, he did not meet me neither, but he was there with me — on the big hill, and how he made me sell him the cow, and told me the bottle was the only thing for me?"

"Yes, indeed, the only thing for you, you fool!" said Molly, seizing the bottle to hurl it at her poor husband's head; but Mick caught it, and quietly (for he minded the old man's advice) loosened his wife's grasp, and placed the bottle again in his bosom. Poor Molly sat down crying while Mick told her his story, with many a crossing and blessing between him and harm. His wife could not help believing him, particularly as she had as much faith in fairies as she had in the priest, who indeed never discouraged her belief in the fairies; maybe he didn't know she believed in them, and maybe he believed in them himself. She got up, however, without saying one word, and began to sweep the earthen floor with a bunch of heath; then she tidied up everything, and put out the long table, and spread the clean cloth, for she had only one, upon it, and Mick, placing the bottle on the ground, looked at it and said:

"Bottle, do your duty."

"Look there! Look there, Mammy!" said his chubby eldest son, a boy about five years old. "Look there! Look there!" And he sprang to his mother's side as two tiny little fellows rose like light from the bottle, and in an instant covered the table with dishes and plates of gold and silver, full of the finest victuals that ever were seen, and when all was done went into the bottle again. Mick and his wife looked at everything with astonishment; they had never seen such plates and dishes before, and didn't think they could ever admire them enough; the very sight almost took away their appetites; but at length Molly said:

"Come and sit down, Mick, and try and eat a bit, sure you ought to be hungry after such a good day's work."

"Why, then, the man told no lie about the bottle."

Mick sat down, after putting the children to the table, and they made a hearty meal, though they couldn't taste half the dishes.

"Now," says Molly, "I wonder will those two good little gentlemen carry away these fine things again?"

They waited, but no one came; so Molly put up the dishes and plates very carefully, saying, "Why, then, Mick, that was no lie sure enough; but you'll be a rich man yet, Mick Purcell."

Mick and his wife and children went to their beds, not to sleep, but to settle about selling the fine things they did not want, and to take more land. Mick went to Cork and sold his plate, and bought a horse and cart, and began to show that he was making money; and they did all they could to keep the bottle a secret; but for all that their landlord found it out, for he came to Mick one day and asked him where he got all his money — sure it was not by the farm; and he bothered him so much that at last Mick told him of the bottle. His landlord offered him a deal of money for it, but Mick would not give it, till at last he offered to give him all his farm forever; so Mick, who was very rich, thought he'd never want any more money, and gave him the bottle. But Mick was mistaken — he and his family spent money as if there was no end of it; and to make the story short, they became poorer and poorer, till at last they had nothing left but one cow; and Mick once more drove his cow before him to sell her at Cork fair, hoping to meet the old man and get another bottle. It was hardly daybreak when he left home, and he walked on at a good pace till he reached the big hill: the mists were sleeping in the valleys and curling like smoke wreaths upon the brown heath around him. The sun rose on his left, and just at his feet a lark sprang from its grassy couch and poured forth its joyous matin song, ascending into the clear blue sky

> "Till its form like a speck in the airiness blending,
> And thrilling with music, was melting in light."

Mick crossed himself, listening as he advanced to the sweet song of the lark, but thinking, notwithstanding, all the time of the little old man; when, just as he reached the summit of the hill, he cast his eyes over the extensive prospect before and around him, he was startled and rejoiced by the same well-known voice:

"Well, Mick Purcell, I told you you would be a rich man."

"Indeed, then, sure enough I was, that's no lie for you, sir. Good morning to you, but it is not rich I am now — but have you another bottle, for I want it now as much as I did long ago? So if you have it, sir, here is the cow for it."

"And here is the bottle," said the old man, smiling, "you know what to do with it."

"Oh! Then, sure I do, as good right I have."

"Well, farewell forever, Mick Purcell; I told you you would be a rich man."

"And goodbye to you, sir," said Mick, as he turned back; "and good luck to you, and good luck to the big hill — it wants a name, Bottle Hill — goodbye, sir, goodbye." So Mick walked back as fast as he could, never looking after the white-faced little gentleman and the cow, so anxious was he to bring home the bottle. Well, he arrived with it safely enough, and called out as soon as he saw Molly:

"Oh, sure, I've another bottle!"

"Arrah, then, have you? Why then, you're a lucky man, Mick Purcell, that's what you are."

In an instant she put everything right; and Mick, looking at his bottle, exultingly cried out:

"Bottle, do your duty!"

In a twinkling, two great stout men with big cudgels issued from the bottle (I do not know how they got room in it), and belabored poor Mick and his wife and all his family, till they lay on the floor, when in they went again.

Mick, as soon as he recovered, got up and looked about him; he thought and thought, and at last he took up his wife and his children; and leaving them to recover as well as they could, he took the bottle under his coat and went to his landlord, who had a great company: he got a servant to tell him he wanted to speak to him, and at last he came out to Mick.

"Well, what do you want now?"

"Nothing, sir, only I have another bottle."

"Oh, ho! Is it as good as the first?"

"Yes, sir, and better; if you like, I will show it to you before all the ladies and gentlemen."

"Come along, then."

So saying, Mick was brought into the great hall, where he saw his old bottle standing high up on a shelf. "Ah! Ha!" says he to himself. "Maybe I won't have you by-and-by."

"Now," says the landlord, "show us your bottle."

Mick set it on the floor and uttered the words. In a moment the landlord was tumbled on the floor; ladies and gentlemen, servants and all, were running, and roaring, and sprawling, and

kicking, and shrieking. Wine cups and salvers were knocked
about in every direction, until the landlord called out:

"Stop those two devils, Mick Purcell, or I'll have you hanged!"

"They never shall stop," said Mick, "till I get my own bottle
that I see up there at the top of that shelf."

"Give it down to him, give it down to him, before we are all
killed!" says the landlord.

Mick put his bottle into his bosom; in jumped the two men
into the new bottle, and he carried them home. I need not
lengthen my story by telling how he got richer than ever, how
his son married his landlord's only daughter, how he and his wife
died when they were very old, and how some of the servants,
fighting at their wake, broke the bottles; but still the hill has
the name upon it, ay, and so 'twill be always Bottle Hill to the
end of the world, and so it ought, for it is a strange story.

Wonder
Tales

Ceatach and Blackbird

*T*HERE WERE two warriors there a long time ago and they fell in love with the same girl. But they had such an affection and regard for one another that they would not fall out with one another for the sake of any woman. They both followed the same trade; they were blacksmiths. At that time every man followed a trade.

"Let the man who is the best hand at his trade have the girl," said Ceatach.

"I'm satisfied with that," said Blackbird, "and let each of us do three pieces of work, and whoever succeeds in doing the best bit of work, let him have the woman; and you can have the first turn."

"Very well," said Ceatach, "since you are giving me the first turn, I will let you have the first blow at me undefended if we ever come to fight."

Ceatach started and it wasn't long till he sent out a shower of wheat from his smith's fire. Then Blackbird sent out from his forge fire a hen with a clutch of chickens and they ate up the wheat. Ceatach began again and he sent out from the fire a fox who ate the hen and her clutch of chickens.

"I'm beaten," said Blackbird; "let you have the woman."

Ceatach took the woman with him and they went on board a ship. He raised the slapping, dappling sails. He did not leave a

CEATACH AND BLACKBIRD

mast without bending nor an oar without nearly breaking, plowing the fierce, billowy sea until evening was drawing on and the sun was going behind the shade of the hill. He went up to the top of the mast then and he saw a small island out in front of him. When he came close to the island he went to the rudder and guided the ship on till she leaped up on the dry land. He put the fastening of a year and a day on the ship, even though he might only be ashore for one hour, and he kindled a fire and he cooked the supper for himself and his wife.

He started then to build a castle in which there was no under rafter to be seen inside, nor no over rafter to be seen outside, but one single rafter binding and securing all of them together. There wasn't a castle in the whole world made like it. It was on Finn Mac Cool's land that he built the castle.

One day when Finn went out hunting what did he see before him but Ceatach's castle, and he wondered greatly at it. He called Conan Maol and he said to him:

"Go off, Conan, and find out for me who built that castle there on my land without any permission from me."

When Conan came to the castle he saw Ceatach's wife and he began courting her. Ceatach came out and he gave him a clout behind the ear that put him out on the road. Then he caught him by the two ankles and he put him spinning back to where he came from.

"Are you hurt, Conan?" asked Finn.

"I'm not dead anyway," said Conan. "The man who built the castle sends you word to send three hundred men to fight against him in front, three hundred to attack him on the left hand and three hundred against him on the right, and he will make one day's work of killing them all. And Finn," said Conan, "the most beautiful woman in the world is his wife."

"Indeed, confound you bald-headed, Conan," said Finn, "if it isn't you are the great seeker after women!"

"Goll Mor," said Finn, "go you to that castle and bring me back a proper account of the man that is there."

Goll Mor went off then, and he said to Ceatach that Finn Mac Cool had sent him to find out why he had put a castle there, on Finn's land, without his permission.

"Tell Finn Mac Cool and the whole band of the Fianna to come to dinner tomorrow, and that if he wishes to put a rent on me I'll pay it with a good will," said Ceatach.

On the following day Finn and the Fianna came to Ceatach's castle, and there was a fine dinner ready before them. As soon as they sat down Finn noticed that Ceatach had a valuable goblet and he asked him:

"Is not that my goblet you have?"

"It is not yours," said Ceatach. "Cannot another man have a drinking cup as well as you?"

"I thought it was the one I had lost a while back, as it is very like it."

"In what place did you lose that goblet, Finn?" said Ceatach.

"I lost it on a beach in Kerry," said Finn. "Five warriors took it from me when I was unarmed and alone."

"Go on drinking," said Ceatach, "and if the drinking cup is to be got I will get it for you."

He left Finn and the Fianna then. He went off with a run. He went over hills with a hop, over mountains with a leap, and it wasn't long till he came to the place where Finn had lost his goblet. He found the five warriors drinking out of it and he took the heads off them on the spot. He came back to Finn with the goblet in his hand and he said:

"Isn't this the goblet you lost?"

"Where did you find it?" asked Finn.

"In the place where you lost it," said he, "and I killed the five who took it from you."

"Indeed," said Finn, "I have a runner as good as ever anyone had in the world, and he wouldn't be halfway there since."

"You never had a runner as good as I am," said Ceatach.

"Well now," said Finn, "I have a man building a ship for me in Kerry, and I'll bet my goblet against your goblet that my runner will take a letter to the shipwrights, and that he will be back before you."

"I'll take the bet," said Ceatach.

Finn wrote two letters then and he gave one of them to Keelta, for that was the name of Finn's runner, and he gave the other one to Ceatach. The two went off and they ran side by side till they came to a big wood, and a thorn stuck in Ceatach's foot when he was going through the wood. He tried to pull the thorn out, but it failed him to do so.

"I must go back home," said he to Keelta, "to get my wife to pull this thorn out of my foot."

"I'll beat you easily in that case," said Keelta.

"You will not," said Ceatach, and with that he went back home to his wife. When the thorn was taken out of his foot he started out again, and it wasn't long till he caught up with Keelta, and passed him out. He went to the shipwrights and gave them the letter and he got an answer from them to take back to Finn. Then he bought a ship's mast from them and he put it up on his shoulder. He was halfway back home when he met Keelta, who was tired and worn-out by this time. Ceatach threw Keelta up on his shoulder, and with Keelta on one shoulder and the mast on the other, Ceatach made for his castle where Finn and the Fianna were sitting.

"Let me walk now," said Keelta, when they were coming near Ceatach's castle.

When Ceatach arrived the wonder of the world came over Finn and the Fianna that he should be back so soon. Ceatach left the mast down off his shoulder and he gave the shipwright's letter to Finn.

That night Finn Mac Cool put his thumb of knowledge into his mouth and he chewed it to the marrow. The knowledge came to him then that there was not a man in the whole world half as good as Ceatach.

A little while after that it happened that there was war between Finn and the King of the Greeks, and Finn got his fleet of ships ready to go to Greece. He asked Ceatach to come with him in his own ship.

"I cannot go with you," said Ceatach, "without my wife's permission. My wife combs her hair but once in seven years, and she is combing it now. If you go into her on your two knees maybe you will get permission for me to go with you."

"I have never humbled to any woman before this," said Finn, "but I will do it now."

Finn went in then to where Ceatach's wife was combing her hair with a golden comb, and he was on his two knees. He asked her to let Ceatach go with him to the land of the Greeks.

"I am loath to let him go with you," said the woman, "and if it were not yourself who is asking me I would not let him go. But you will have to promise me one thing."

"What is that?" asked Finn.

"You have white sails on your ship," said she. "Well, if my husband is killed in Greece, you are to put black sails up on your masts when you will be coming home."

Finn promised that he would do as she asked. He took Ceatach away with him then in his own ship, and he did not stop nor stay till he came into the quayside in the land of Greece. There was a giant there who was called the Great Giant of Greece, and it was this giant who was to be the first to fight against Finn. Ceatach went off with himself and he left Finn after him while he went to the place where the giant was. The giant was looking out through the window, and Ceatach gave him such a blow with his fist that it broke every tooth he had in his head.

"You have a hard fist," said the giant. "What are you wanting from me?"

"Bread, wine and lodging," said Ceatach.

"There's a baker and a tavern keeper and a lodging house down there below you, and they can give you everything you want, if they wish to," said the giant.

Ceatach went down to them, but they closed their doors in his face. He knocked on the door with his fist and he broke it in pieces. The baker got afraid and he said:

"I have only one pound of bread for each man of my master's following."

"And I have only one pint of wine for each man of them," said the tavern keeper. "But here is a drink of pot ale for you."

"Take the froth off it," said Ceatach.

The tavern keeper put the quart measure up on his head, to drink off the froth, and Ceatach drew back his fist and he struck the quart measure. If he did he sent it through the head of the tavern keeper so that it killed him. Then he took away with him three hundred loaves of bread and a barrel of wine for Finn and the Fianna, and they spent a merry night.

On the following morning Ceatach went to the giant's house and he leveled the pole of combat. The noise he made with it did not leave a child in woman or calf in cow within seven miles of them that it did not cause to turn around. The giant came out and asked:

"What do you want?"

"A fight," said Ceatach.

They attacked each other then. They made hard places soft and soft places hard, and they drew wells of spring water out of the gray stones with their fighting. Seven days and seven nights they were at it. Each of them was greatly worn out, but neither of them had got the upper hand of the other. Then the giant spoke:

"We should stop the fight for one day."

"Be it so," said Ceatach. He agreed because he had a deep wound in his side.

On the morning of the following day Ceatach was going over a wall when he fell, and the dew on the grass cured the wound in his side. He came then to the middle of the wood where there was a little house with no one in it but a little old man who used to be a steward to the giant.

"Welcome, Ceatach, son of the King of Pleasure!" said the old man. "It was a long hard battle you fought with the giant, but I'll have you know that nothing will kill that giant but his own sword."

"If you can get that sword for me, I'll make you king of this country," said Ceatach.

"I'll try to get it for you," said the old man.

He went off then and Ceatach did not know where he had gone. But where had he gone to but to the Great Giant, and he said to him:

"That man who has been fighting with you for seven days and seven nights I have killed today, O Master. I have buried him and I have put seven tons of stones over his grave."

"Good man!" said the Great Giant, and with that he fell back and went to sleep, for he was very weary after the seven days' fighting. As soon as the old man saw that the giant was asleep he stole the sword from him and he went off and gave it to Ceatach.

On the following morning Ceatach went to the Great Giant's house and he struck the pole of combat. The Great Giant came out and he had a new sword in his hand. He had no courage left at all when he saw Ceatach before him, and he shouted out as quickly as he could:

"I declare peace with yourself, with Finn Mac Cool and with the whole of the Fianna of Erin."

"I will not make any peace with you," said Ceatach and he took the head off him.

He called out then to the old man who had been the giant's steward and he told him he was making him king of the country from that on. He drew a withe through the Great Giant's head and took it off to Finn. When they saw him coming with the giant's head over his shoulder, and he himself safe and sound, the Fianna gave him a great welcome.

"Now," said Finn, "since the Great Giant of Greece is dead we may as well set out and go back to Erin, and you will come in my boat, Ceatach."

They hoisted the dappled, slapping sails then and they put the stern of the boat to the land and its prow to the sea, and they plowed the strong, billowy waves, and the whales sang fairy music for them as they went.

On the morning of the next day Ceatach said to Finn: "I had a bad dream last night, Finn. Blackbird, the son of the King of Scotland, is coming to kill me today, in order to get my wife."

"If he comes near this ship," said Finn, "I'll take the head off him."

"It is not in the power of any man in Erin to kill him. And until he takes the head off me," said Ceatach, "I cannot defend my head against him, for I promised him the first blow. But I will make two halves of his body just as he takes my head off."

They were not too long sailing the next day when Blackbird

came over the water in a fiery coach. He had a drawn sword in his hand so Ceatach drew his sword too. Each of them struck one blow against the other. Blackbird took the head off Ceatach and Ceatach made two halves of Blackbird, and he fell out of the fiery coach and down onto the deck of the ship. Finn Mac Cool threw him into the sea. He took up Ceatach then and he laid him down carefully, both head and body, in the hold of the ship. When they reached the harbor and came alongside the quay in Erin, Ceatach's wife was waiting for them on board her own ship.

"Where's Ceatach?" she asked.

"Down below in the hold," said Finn.

"He is dead," said the woman, "or he would be here on the deck to welcome me."

"My bitter sorrow that he is dead," said Finn.

"I told you to raise black sails if he were dead," said Ceatach's wife.

"I was afraid to do that," said Finn.

She went on board Finn's ship then and she took Ceatach's body and head with her to her own ship. She put the prow to the sea and the stern to the land and she sailed away and there was no one with her on the ship.

When the daylight was fading she came to an island. She saw a castle on the island and she drew her ship up on the beach. She went towards the castle and she saw two warriors inside. One of them got up from the chair he was sitting on and he gave it to her.

"Is there any woman here in this castle with you?" she asked.

"There is not indeed," said one of them. "There are giants on this island and they would not allow us to marry."

"Oh," said she, "my seven hundred blessings on the man that would not leave those giants long alive if he were here!"

"Where is that man?" asked one of the warriors.

"He is dead, with the head cut from his body, on board my ship," she said.

"We can bring him back to life again," said they.

"If you can then do so," said she. "And I promise you that he will make short work of killing the giants for you tomorow."

They took a pot of healing balm and they asked her to bring them to where her husband was. She took them on board and she showed them were Ceatach lay dead. They put the healing balm on him and he rose up healthy and strong again. But with the hurry they were in they put his head on the wrong way. His face was where the back of his head should be, and the back of his head was where his face should be.

"Woe is me," said Ceatach's wife, "it would be better for him to be dead than to be the way he is now."

"Have patience, woman," said one of the warriors, "and we will settle his head right on him."

One of them cut the head off Ceatach again with a stroke of his sword, and then he put it back on him facing the right way as it should be. Then they gave him and his wife a hundred thousand welcomes and they spent that night making merry — a third of it in telling stories, a third telling Fenian romances and a third in pleasant slumber and sweet sleep.

In the morning Ceatach rose early. He ate and drank all he wanted and he said to the two warriors:

"Show me those giants."

"We would not like to go too near them. They are in that castle down there at the foot of that hill yonder."

"Very well," said Ceatach.

He walked down to the door of the fortress and he struck the pole of combat. It was not long till the giants came out.

"What do you want?" they asked.

"I want to take the heads off the three of you," he said. "Send out your best man to me first."

One of the giants came out then and it wasn't long till Ceatach took the head off him. Then two of them attacked him together, and they were fighting till the sun went down behind the shade of the hill, when Ceatach killed the two of them. He went back to the house of the two warriors at nightfall, carrying the heads of the three giants over his shoulder.

On the following morning Ceatach and his wife said goodbye to the two warriors and they went aboard their ship to sail back to Erin. A great storm arose in the sea and a big whale got under the ship. He raised it high up on his back and he swam off with the ship like that on his back as if it were on dry land, and he never stopped till he came to the western country and there he left them. Ceatach and his wife fixed their boat on the beach and got out on the land where they walked around to see the countryside. Then the darkness of night began to gather around them and just then they saw a big house on the side of the road.

"Go in and ask for lodgings for the night," said Ceatach's wife.

He went in and he knocked at the door. A gray-haired old man came out and asked them what they wanted.

"Lodgings for the night for myself and my wife," said Ceatach.

"The lord of the house is not at home, but I have a little small house down there below, and you can stay there till morning," said the old man.

Ceatach and his wife went down to the little house and they found a fire lighting there before them. They sat down at the fire and after half an hour the old man came in. He prepared a fine meal for them and gave them a bed.

Early in the morning the old man got up. Ceatach and his wife rose too, but the old man told them not to go without seeing the lord. He left them then and he went up to his master in the big house and he said to him:

"There is a man and his wife below in my little house and there is not a woman in the world as beautiful as she!"

The nobleman sent for a wise, blind man that was there and he asked him how he might get the beautiful woman for himself.

"That man has great strength and he could conquer any man in this kingdom. Ask him and his wife to dinner today and I will put herbs in his wine that will put him asleep for twenty-four hours. Tie him up well then and take the head off him. There is no other way to get the woman from him."

The old man went and brought Ceatach and his wife to the nobleman. When the nobleman saw Ceatach's wife he fell in love with her, and he said to Ceatach that it would please him if the two of them would have dinner with him that night.

Ceatach said they would and they began to converse. He told the nobleman how the whale had brought them to that country.

"I know that whale well," said the nobleman. "He is the son of High Scotland and he has the power of magic. A man named Ceatach, son of the King of Pleasure, killed him."

"Isn't it a great wonder that he let anyone kill him when he has the power of magic," said Ceatach.

"Ceatach would kill the devil himself!" said the nobleman, without knowing that it was to Ceatach himself he was talking.

When the dinner was put on the table they began eating and drinking, and before Ceatach had taken the second drink he fell under the table. He had no senses left, but as little as if he were a dead man. The lord had his men come in then and he said to them:

"Tie him up and give me my axe until I will cut the head off him."

They gave him the axe and he had it drawn back over his shoulder to strike the blow when Ceatach's wife spoke:

"Do not kill him, but throw him out on the sea."

"Very well," said the nobleman, "let us throw him into the sea!"

His wife then bent down and put a ring on one of Ceatach's fingers. That ring had certain powers. Whoever wore it could neither drown, nor choke, nor die of want.

They took Ceatach's body up to a cliff overhanging the sea and they threw it down on the waves. There was a bush growing out of the side of the cliff and the body fell into the bush and settled there. In that bush there was a griffon's nest and there were two nestlings in it. Ceatach fell very close to that nest.

He awoke after a long time and he couldn't make out where he was. He was very hungry. He saw the two old birds giving food to the two young ones in the nest. The little birds used to open their mouths and the old birds used to put the pieces of food into them. So Ceatach opened his mouth and he used to get a piece from them too as well as the nestlings.

One day the old birds did not come and he was so hungry that he killed one of the nestlings and ate it. On the following day the old birds did not come either. He killed the other nestling and ate that too. His hunger left him.

On the evening of that same day Finn Mac Cool and some of the Fianna were going past the cliff in their ships and Finn noticed the big nest that was in the bush. He told Goll and bald-headed Conan to go up and see what was the strange thing that was in the big nest.

They went ashore and went halfway up the cliff to the bush and they found Ceatach inside in the nest. They thought he was a wild man. They brought him down and took him on board the ship, bound and tied up as he was.

"Who are you?" asked Finn.

"Unbind me, shave me, put clothes on me, and then I will tell you who I am," said Ceatach.

They did as he asked. Ceatach stretched out his limbs, shook himself and said:

"Don't you recognize me now, Finn? I am Ceatach, son of the King of Pleasure, though it is little pleasure I have had for a long time."

"O love of my heart," said Finn, "we thought you were dead."

"If I was I came to life again," said he. Then he told them everything that had happened to him since he had been beheaded by Blackbird on board Finn's ship.

"We will go ashore now and we will kill that treacherous nobleman," said Finn.

"You have the gift of knowledge, Finn," said Ceatach. "Find out for me how is my wife."

Finn put his thumb of knowledge into his mouth then and he chewed it almost to the marrow. The knowledge came to him that Ceatach's wife was in the lord's castle, and she had put him under bonds not to marry her until a year and a day had passed since Ceatach had been thrown into the sea.

"If that is so,"said Ceatach, "I will be able to return with you to Erin, and I will be back here again before the year and a day has passed. Then I'll have some fun with that nobleman!"

He went back to Erin with Finn and he spent the time eating and drinking with the Fianna until the year and a day were almost up. Then he got a ship from Finn and he did not stop nor stay until he came to the western land. He went straight to the house of the old man who had given him and his wife lodging the year before. But the old man did not know him, for he was dressed up as a piper this time and he had bagpipes with him.

"Have you any news?" he asked the old man.

"My master is getting married tonight," said he, "and you will get any amount to eat and drink at the big house, and they will pay you well for your music."

"Have you any big bag?" asked Ceatach.

"I have an empty wool sack," said the old man. "You can take that with you."

He took the wool sack with him and he came to the castle as night was falling. He went and stood outside, before the big door, and he began to play his bagpipes. The nobleman himself came out to him and he told him to go in and that he would get the full of his bag.

Ceatach went in and he did not leave a mouthful on the table that he did not put into his bag, and he threw the bag down to the house of the old man. His wife knew then that it was Ceatach that was there, and she gave him a glass of wine. The nobleman got very angry when he saw her giving a drink to the piper and he gave her a box on the ear.

Ceatach grabbed him by the two ankles; he swung him around and began to beat all the people that were there with him, until he had killed or knocked down every one of them and the lord with them. The priest who was going to marry the nobleman and Ceatach's wife cleared out the door, and it is likely that he has never stopped running since.

On the morning after that Ceatach and his wife went aboard their ship. They raised the slapping, dappling sails and they started plowing the fierce, strong waves until they came safely back to Erin. Finn and the Fianna gave them a rousing welcome there. They lived happily in Erin after that till the day of their deaths.

King of Lies

*T*HERE WAS a widow there one time and she had seven sons. The first son was so small that a March foal could not get a grip on the top of his hair and he grazing in a pasture barer than anyone ever saw; the second son was the same height as the grass, and the third was that small that he was not tall enough to tie the gad of the hames on his mother's donkey unless he stood up on a stool. The fourth son was like any other man, the fifth was as high as the moon, the sixth was so tall that he had to wear a soft cap always, for fear he would split open the sky. And the seventh was so tall that he could never stand up, but he had always to go on his hands and knees while the back of his rump rubbed against the sky.

At this time there was a king in the Eastern World and he had one daughter, the most beautiful woman that could be found on land or on sea. The king was growing old and he pledged his word that he would give his daughter in marriage to the first man who would compel him to say: "You told a lie," or "You told your first lie." The people who used to make fun of him used to call him "The King of Lies," because they knew he had not the cunning to make up even one lie.

One of the widow's sons set out for his court to try to win his daughter. On the day he arrived the king took him out walking around the place and he showed him his cows.

"I'll bet," said the king, "that you have never seen that number of cows all together like this in your life before."

"Well, indeed, why shouldn't I?" said the widow's son. "My mother has so many cows at home that the buttermilk we have left after making the butter would turn seven hundred millwheels."

The king never said a word but went on listening to him. The next day the king took the widow's son out and showed him his bees.

"I'll lay a wager with you today," said the king, "that you have never before set eyes on so many beehives."

"Indeed," said the widow's son, "they are nothing to what my mother has at home."

"All the same," said the king, "your mother never gets as much honey from her bees as I do."

"Don't be talking of honey," said the widow's son, "for your talk is idle talk. It is I who am in charge of my mother's hives and she has seven hundred thousand of them. I have to count all the bees the first thing in the morning, for fear any one of them would stay inside in the hive through idleness or bad health, and at night again for fear any of them would stay out from us. One evening I was a bee short, so as soon as all the others were sitting down quietly at ease inside in their hives, I went looking for the one that was missing. I went up the hill and I met a nag. I caught him and jumped up on his back and I started off and never stopped till I came to a wood. There was my bee inside in a big tree fine and comfortable for herself. I cut some thin willows and made two baskets. I threw the two creels over the back of the nag, and I filled them both up to the tip-top with my honey — the honey of a single day's making. I caught the bee then and I laid her down on the back of the nag, between the two creels. With the great load that was on him the back of the nag broke. I got a big long staff of oak then and thrust it into his mouth, down his throat and out through his back, and I drove him home with the load of honey."

The king never said a word but listened to all the widow's son was telling him, though he found it hard to keep silent. The third day they went out together again to look at a beanstalk the king had growing.

"Isn't that a fine beanstalk?" said the king.

" 'Tis fine and high," said the widow's son, "but you never saw the like of my mother's beanstalk, every shoot of it growing up high into the air, up, up to the sky! Don't I climb up three branches of it every Sunday morning to hear Mass in heaven. One Sunday when I was up there a great storm blew up and broke every leaf and branch of that beanstalk. I took up lodgings for the night where I was. On the following morning I started to go down and I came on three women who were winnowing oats near the threshold of the door to heaven. 'Will you oblige me with the makings of a straw rope?' I said to them. 'We will to be sure,' said they and they gave it to me. I twisted the straw into a fine strong rope and I hung it on the sky and I let myself down without any bother. All went well till I came near the end of the rope, and by then every bit of twist was gone out of it. When I came to that part the rope broke on me and I was pitched down on top of my head. Just as I was about three yards from the ground a fox jumped up and snapped the head clean off of me. I ran after him and grabbed him by the tail, and as I ran I gave him seven hundred kicks and he let out seven hundred squeaks, and every one of those squeaks was seven hundred times more of a man than you were ever a king."

"You've said your first lie!" said the king. "And it wasn't the first, for you've told thousands of thundering lies."

"Take it easy!" said the widow's son. "I have won your daughter now."

"You have," said the king, "but may neither of you ever prosper, and may ye not be long together!"

The widow's son and the king's daughter were married, and I do not think that the old man's bad wish fell on them, for they lived together till they were both as gray as mice.

Blaiman, Son of Apple, in the Kingdom of the White Strand

*T*HERE WAS a king in Erin long ago who had two sons and one daughter. On a day of days, the daughter walked into her father's garden, in which she saw an apple tree with only one apple on it; she took the apple and ate it.

There was an old druid in the castle who saw the king's daughter going out, and met her coming in.

"Well," said he, "you had the look of a maiden when you were going out, and you have the look of a married woman coming in."

Those who were near heard the saying of the druid, and it was going the rounds till it came to the king. The king went at once to the druid, and asked, "What is this that you say about my daughter?"

"I say nothing," answered the druid.

"You must tell me your words," said the king, "and prove them, or lose your head."

"Oh, as you are going that far you must give me time, and if a few months do not prove my words true, you may cut the head off me."

The princess was then taken to the top of the king's castle, where no one could see her but her maid. There she remained till she gave birth to a son with a golden spot on his poll, and a silver spot on his forehead. He was so beautiful that if sunshine and breeze ever rested on a child, they would rest on him; and what of him did not grow in the day grew at night. He grew so quickly that soon he was as large as the king's sons, his uncles, and rose out to be a great champion.

One day when the two sons of the king were hunting, there was snow on the ground, and they killed a hare. Some of the hare's blood fell on the snow, and they said that that was a beautiful meeting of colors. They were wondering could any woman be found with such colors on her face, white shining through the red. When they came home in the evening, they asked the old druid could a woman of that sort be found. He answered that if she could itself, little good would it do them; they could find wives good enough for them near home. They said that that was no matter, but to tell them where was the woman they had asked for.

"That woman," said the druid, "is the daughter of the king of the kingdom of the White Strand. Hundreds of champions have lost their heads for her; and if you go, you will lose your heads too."

The elder son said: "We do not mind that; we will go."

The brothers had no vessel to take them to the kingdom of the White Strand; and the elder said he would build one. He took tools one morning, and started for the seashore. When just outside the castle, he heard a voice asking:

"Where are you going, king's son?"

"I am going to make a turkey pen," answered the young man.

"May you prosper in justice and truth," said the voice.

The king's son began to build the ship that day; and in the evening what had he built but a turkey pen? When he came home, they asked what had he made.

BLAIMAN, SON OF APPLE

"Nothing; I made only a turkey pen."

"Oh," said the second son, "you are a fool. I knew that you could do nothing good."

On the following morning, the second son started for the seashore; and the voice spoke to him, and asked:

"Where are you going, king's son?"

"To build a pigsty," answered he.

"May you prosper in justice and truth," said the voice.

He worked all day; and in the evening it was a pigsty that he had. He came home; and now the brothers were doleful because they had not a ship in which to sail to the princess.

The following morning, the king's grandson said: "Give me the tools, to see can I myself do anything."

"What can you do, you fool?" asked the uncles.

"That matters not," replied he.

He left the castle; and at the place where the voice spoke to his uncles, it spoke to him also, and asked:

"What are you going to do, Blaiman, son of Apple?" (He did not know his origin till then.)

"I am going to build a ship," said Blaiman.

"That it may thrive with you in justice and truth," said the voice.

He went off to the edge of a wood that was growing at the seashore, gave one blow to a tree, and it went to its own proper place in the vessel. In the evening Blaiman had the nicest ship that ever moved on the deep sea. When finished, the ship was at the edge of the shore; he gave it one blow of a sledge, and sent it out to deep water. Blaiman went home full of gladness.

"What have you made?" asked the uncles.

"Go out and see for yourselves," answered Blaiman.

The two went and saw the ship in the harbor. They were delighted to see the fine vessel, as they themselves could not build it. The voice had built it with Blaiman in return for his truth.

Next morning provisions for a day and a year were placed in the vessel. The two sons of the king went on board, raised the sails, and were moving out toward the great ocean. Blaiman saw the ship leaving and began to cry; he was sorry that, after building the ship, it was not he who had the first trial of his own work. When his mother heard him, she grew sorry too, and asked what trouble was on him; and he told her that after he had built the ship, he wanted to have the first trial of it.

"You are foolish," said she. "You are only a boy yet; your bones are not hard. You must not think of going to strange countries."

He answered that nothing would do him but to go. The old king, the grandfather, wanted Blaiman to stay, but he would not.

"Well," said the king, "what I have not done for another I will do now for you. I will give you my sword; and you will never be put back by any man while you keep that blade."

Blaiman left the house then; the vessel was outside the harbor already. He ran to the mouth of the harbor, and, placing the point of his sword on the brink of the shore, gave one leap out on board. The two uncles were amazed when they saw what their nephew had done, and were full of joy at having him with them. They turned the ship's prow to the sea, and the stern to land. They raised to the tops of the hard, tough, stained masts the great sweeping sails, and took their capacious, smoothly polished vessel past harbors with gentle sloping shores, and there the ship left behind it pale green wavelets. Then, with a mighty wind, they went through great flashing, stern-dashing waves with such force that not a nail in the ship was unheated, or a

finger on a man inactive; and so did the ship hurry forward that
its stern rubbed its prow, and it raised before it, by dint of sailing, a proud, haughty ridge through the middle of the fair, red
sea.

When the wind failed, they sat down with the oars of fragrant
beech or white ash, and with every stroke they sent the ship forward three leagues on the sea, where fishes, seals, and monsters
rose around them, making music and sport, and giving courage to
the men; and the three never stopped nor cooled until they
sailed into the kingdom of the White Strand. Then they drew
their vessel to a place where no wave was striking, nor wind
rocking it, nor the sun splitting it, nor even a crow of the air
dropping upon it; but a clean strand before it, and coarse sand
on which wavelets were breaking. They cast two anchors towards the sea, and one toward land, and gave the vessel the fix-
ing of a day and a full year, though they might not be absent
more than one hour.

On the following day they saw one wide forest as far as the
eye could reach; they knew not what manner of land was it.

"Would you go and inquire," said Blaiman to the elder uncle,
"what sort of a country that is inside?"

The uncle went in, very slowly, among the trees, and at last,
seeing flashes of light through the forest, rushed back in terror,
the eyes starting out of his head.

"What news have you?" asked Blaiman.

"I saw flashes of fire, and could not go farther," said the elder
king's son.

"Go you," said Blaiman to the other, "and bring some account of the country."

He did not go much farther than the elder brother, then
came back, and said: "We may as well sail home again."

"Well," said Blaiman, "ye have provisions for a day and a

year in this vessel. I will go now, and do ye remain here; if I am not back before the end of the day and the year, wait no longer."

He gave them goodbye, then went on, and entered the forest. It was not long till he met with the flashes. He did not mind them, but went forward; and when he had gone a good distance, he found the trees farther apart and scattered. Leaving the trees, he came out on a broad, open plain; in the middle of the plain was a castle; in front of the castle twelve champions practicing at feats of arms; and it was the flashes from the blows of their swords that he and his uncles had seen in the forest. So skilled were the champions that not one of them could draw a drop of blood from another.

Blaiman was making toward them. By the side of the path there was a small hut, and as he was passing the door, an old woman came out and hailed him. He turned, and she said:

"A hundred thousand welcomes to you, Blaiman, son of Apple, from Erin."

"Well, good woman," said Blaiman, "you have the advantage. You know me, but I have no knowledge of you."

"I know you well," said she, "and it's sorry I am that you are here. Do you see those twelve men out there opposite? You are going to make for them now; but rest on your legs, and let the beginning of another day come to you."

"Your advice may be good," said Blaiman, and he went in. The old woman prepared his supper as well as it was ever prepared at his grandfather's house at home, and prepared a bed for him as good as ever he had. He slept enough, and he wanted it. When day overtook him on the morrow, he rose, and washed his face and hands, and asked mercy and help from God, and if he did not he let it alone; and the old woman prepared breakfast in the best way she could, and it was not the wrong way. He

went off then in good courage to the castle of the king; and there
was a pole of combat in front of the castle which a man wanting
combat would strike with his sword. He struck the pole a blow
that was heard throughout the whole kingdom.

"Good, good!" said the king. "The like of that blow was not
struck while I am in this castle."

He put his head through a window above and saw Blaiman
outside.

Around the rear of the castle was a high wall set with iron
spikes. Few were the spikes without heads on them; some heads
were fresh, some with part of the flesh on them, and some were
only bare skulls. It was a dreadful sight to see, and strong was
the man that it would not put fright on.

"What do you want?" asked the king of Blaiman.

"Your daughter to marry, or combat."

" 'Tis combat you will get," said the king; and the twelve
champions of valor were let out at him together. It was pitiful to
see him; each one of the twelve aiming a blow at him, he trying
to defend himself, and he all wounded and hacked by them.
When the day was growing late, he began to be angry; the noble
blood swelled in his breast to be uppermost; and he rose, with
the activity of his limbs, out of the joints of his bones over them,
and with three sweeping blows took the twelve heads off the
champions. He left the place then, deeply wounded, and went
back to the old woman's cabin; and if he did, it was a pleasure
for the old woman to see him. She put him into a caldron of
venom, and then into a caldron of cure. When he came out, he
was perfectly healed; and the old woman said:

"Victory and prosperity to you, my boy. I think you will do
something good, for the twelve were the strongest and ablest of
all the king's forces. You have done more than any man that ever
walked this way before."

They made three parts of the night: the first part, they spent in eating and drinking; the second, in telling tales and singing ballads; the third, in rest and sound sleep.

He had a good sleep, and he needed it. Being anxious, he rose early; and as early as he rose, breakfast was ready before him, prepared by the old woman. He ate his breakfast, went to the king's castle, and struck the pole.

"What do you want?" asked the king, thrusting his head through the window.

"Seven hundred men at my right hand, seven hundred at my left, seven hundred behind me, and as many as on the three sides out before me."

They were sent to him four deep through four gates. He went through them as a hawk through a flock of small birds on a March day, or as a blackbird or a small boy from Iraghti Conor between two thickets. He made lanes and roads through them, and slew them all. He made then a heap of their heads, a heap of their bodies, and a heap of their weapons. Trembling fear came on the king, and Blaiman went to the old woman's cabin.

"Victory and prosperity to you, my boy; you have all his forces stretched now, unless he comes out against you himself; and I'm full sure that he will not. He'll give you the daughter."

She had a good dinner before him. He had fought so well that there was neither spot nor scar on his skin; for he had not let a man of the forty-two hundred come within a sword's length of his body. He passed the night as the previous night.

Next morning after breakfast he went to the castle, and with one blow made wood lice of the king's pole of combat. The king went down to Blaiman, took him under the arm, and, leading him up to the high chamber where the daughter was, put her hand in his.

The king's daughter kissed Blaiman, and embraced him, and

gave him a ring with her name and surname written inside on it. This was their marriage.

Next day Blaiman, thinking that his uncles had waited long enough and might go back to Erin, said to the king:

"I will visit my uncles and then return hither."

His wife, an only child, was heir to the kingdom, and he was to reign with her.

"Oh," said the king, "something else is troubling me now. There are three giants, neighbors of mine, and they are great robbers. All my forces are killed; and before one day passes the giants will be at me, and throw me out of the kingdom."

"Well," said Blaiman, "I will not leave you till I settle the giants; but now tell where they are to be found."

"I will," said the king; and he gave him all needful instruction. Blaiman went first to the house of the youngest giant, where he struck the pole of combat, and the sound was heard over all that giant's kingdom.

"Good, good!" said the giant. "The like of that blow has never been struck on that pole of combat before." And out he came.

"A nerve burning of the heart to you, you miserable wretch!" said the giant to Blaiman. "And great was your impudence to come to my castle at all."

"It is not caring to give you pleasure that I am," said Blaiman, "but to knock a tormenting satisfaction out of your ribs."

"Is it hard, thorny wrestling that you want, or fighting with sharp gray swords in the lower and upper ribs?" asked the giant.

"I will fight with sharp gray swords," said Blaiman.

The giant went in and fitted on his wide, roomy vest, his strong, unbreakable helmet, his cross-worked coat of mail; then he took his bossy, pale red shield and his spear. Every hair on his head and in his beard was so stiffly erect from anger and rage that a small apple or a sloe, an iron apple or a smith's anvil, might stand on each hair of them.

Blaiman fitted on his smooth, flowery stockings, and his two dry, warm boots of the hide of a small cow that was the first calf of another cow that never lay on any one of her sides. He fitted on his single-threaded silken girdle, which three craftsmen had made, underneath his broad-pointed, sharp sword that would not leave a remnant uncut, or, if it did, what it left at the first blow it took at the second. This sword was to be unsheathed with the right hand and sheathed with the left. He gave the first blood of battle as a terrible oath that he himself was the choice champion of the Fenians, the feather of greatness, the slayer of a champion of bravery; a man to compel justice and right, but not give either justice or right; a man who had earned what he owned in the gap of every danger, in the path of every hardship, who was sure to get what belonged to him, or to know who detained it.

They rushed at each then like two bulls of the wilderness, or two wild echoes of the cliff; they made soft ground of the hard, and hard ground of the soft; they made low ground of high, and high ground of low. They made whirling circles of the earth, and millwheels of the sky; and if anyone were to come from the lower to the upper world, it was to see those two that he should come. They were this way at each other to the height of the evening. Blaiman was growing hungry; and through dint of anger he rose with the activity of his limbs, and with one stroke of his sword cut off the giant's head. There was a tree growing near. Blaiman knocked off a tough, slender branch, put one end of it in through the left ear and out through the right, then, putting the head on the sword and the sword on his shoulder, went home to the king. Coming near the castle with the giant's head, he met a man tied in a tree whose name was Hung Up Naked.

"Victory and prosperity to you, young champion," said the man. "You have done well hitherto; now loose me from this."

"Are you long there?" asked Blaiman.

"I am seven years here," answered the other.

"Many a man passed this way during that time. As no man of them loosed you, I will not loose you."

He went home then, and threw down the head by the side of the castle. The head was so weighty that the castle shook to its deepest foundations. The king came to the hall door, shook Blaiman's hand, and kissed him. They spent that night as the previous night; and on the next day he went to meet the second giant, came to his house, and struck the pole of combat. The giant put out his two heads and said:

"You rascal, I lay a wager it was you who killed my young brother yesterday; you'll pay for it now, for I think it is a sufficient length of life to get a glimpse of you, and I know not what manner of death I should give you."

"It is not to offer satisfaction that I am here," said Blaiman, "but to give you the same as your brother."

"Is it any courage you have to fight me?" asked the giant.

"It is indeed," said Blaiman; " 'tis for that I am here."

"What will you have," asked the giant, "hard, thorny wrestling, or fighting with sharp gray swords?"

"I prefer hard, thorny wrestling," said Blaiman, "as I have practiced it on the lawns with noble children."

They seized each other, and made soft places hard, and hard places soft; they drew wells of spring water through the hard, stony ground in such fashion that the place under them was a soft quagmire in which the giant, who was weighty, was sinking.

He sank to his knees. Blaiman then caught hold of him firmly and forced him down to his hips.

"Am I to cut off your heads now?" asked Blaiman.

"Do not do that," said the giant. "Spare me, and I will give you my treasure room and all that I have of gold and silver."

"I will give you your own award," said Blaiman. "If I were in your place, and you in mine, would you let me go free?"

"I would not," said the giant.

Blaiman drew his broad, shadowy sword made in Erin. It had edge, temper, and endurance; and with one blow he took the two heads off the giant, and carried the heads to the castle. He passed by Hung Up Naked, who asked him to loose him, but he refused. When Blaiman threw the heads down, much as the castle shook the first day, it shook more the second.

The king and his daughter were greatly rejoiced. They stifled him with kisses, drowned him with tears, and dried him with stuffs of silk and satin; they gave him the taste of every food and the odor of every drink — Greek honey and Lochlin beer in dry, warm cups, and the taste of honey in every drop of the beer. I bailing it out, it would be a wonder if I myself was not thirsty.

They passed that night as the night before. Next morning Blaiman was very tired and weary after his two days' fight, and the third giant's land was far distant.

"Have you a horse of any kind for me to ride?" asked he of the king.

"Be not troubled," said the king. "There is a stallion in my stable that has not been out for seven years, but fed on red wheat and pure spring water; if you think you can ride that horse, you may take him."

Blaiman went to the stable. When the horse saw the stranger, he bared his teeth back to the ears and made a drive at him to tear him asunder; but Blaiman struck the horse with his fist on the ear and stretched him. The horse rose, but was quiet. Blaiman bridled and saddled him, then drove out that slender, low-sided, bare-shouldered, long-flanked, tame, meek-mannered steed, in which were twelve qualities combined: three of a bull, three of a woman, three of a fox, and three of a hare. Three of a bull — a full eye, a thick neck, and a bold forehead; three of a woman — full hips, slender waist, and a mind for a burden; three of a hare — a swift run against a hill, a sharp turn about, and a high leap; three of a fox — a light, treacherous, proud gait, to take in the two sides of the road by dint of study and acuteness, and to look only ahead. He now went on, and could overtake the wind that was before him; and the wind that was behind, carrying rough hailstones, could not overtake him.

Blaiman never stopped nor stayed till he arrived at the giant's castle; and this giant had three heads. He dismounted and struck the pole a blow that was heard throughout the kingdom. The giant looked out and said:

"Oh, you villain! I'll wager it was you that killed my two brothers. I think it sufficient life to see you, and I don't know yet what manner of death will I put on you."

"It is not to give satisfaction to you that I am here, you vile worm!" said Blaiman. "Ugly is the smile of your laugh; and it must be that your crying will be uglier still."

"Is it hard, thorny wrestling that you want, or fighting with sharp gray swords?" asked the giant.

"I will fight with sharp gray swords," said Blaiman.

They rushed at each other then like two bulls of the wilderness. Toward the end of the afternoon, the heavier blows were falling on Blaiman. Just then a robin came on a bush in front of him and said:

"O Blaiman, son of Apple, from Erin, far away are you from the women who would lay you out and weep over you! There would be no one to care for you unless I were to put two green leaves on your eyes to protect them from the crows of the air. Stand between the sun and the giant, and remember where men draw blood from sheep in Erin."

Blaiman followed the advice of the robin. The two combatants kept at each other; but the giant was blinded by the sun, for he had to bend himself often to look at his foe. One time when he stretched forward, his helmet was lifted a little, Blaiman got a glimpse of his neck, near the ear. That instant he stabbed him. The giant was bleeding till he lost the last of his blood. Then Blaiman cut the three heads off him, and carrried them home on the pommel of his saddle. When he was passing, Hung Up Naked begged for release, but Blaiman refused and went on. Hung Up Naked praised him for his deeds, and continued to praise. On second thought, Blaiman turned back, and began to release Hung Up Naked; but if he did, as fast as he loosened one bond, two squeezed on himself, in such fashion that when he had Hung Up Naked unbound, he was himself doubly bound; he had the binding of five men hard and tough on his body. Hung Up Naked was free now; he mounted Blaiman's steed and rode to the king's castle. He threw down the giant's heads, and never stopped nor stayed till he went to where the king's daughter was, put a finger under her girdle, bore her out of the castle, and rode away swiftly.

Blaiman remained bound for two days to the tree. The king's swineherd came the way and saw Blaiman bound in the tree.

"Ah, my boy," said he, "you are bound there, and Hung Up Naked is freed by you; and if you had passed him as you did twice before, you need not be where you are now."

"It cannot be helped," said Blaiman. "I must suffer."

"Oh, then," said the swineherd, "it is a pity to have you there and me here; I will never leave you till I free you."

Up went the swineherd, and began to loosen Blaiman; and it happened to him as to Blaiman himself; the bonds that had been on Blaiman were now on the swineherd.

"I have heard always that strength is more powerful than magic," said Blaiman. He went at the tree and pulled it up by the roots; then, taking his sword, he made small pieces of the tree, and freed the swineherd.

Blaiman and the swineherd then went to the castle. They found the king sitting by the table, with his head on his hand, and a stream of tears flowing from his eyes to the table, and from the table to the floor.

"What is your trouble?" asked Blaiman.

"Hung Up Naked came and said that it was himself who killed the giant, and he took my daughter."

When he found that his wife was taken, and that he knew not where to look for her, Blaiman was raging.

"Stay here tonight," said the king.

Next morning the king brought a tablecloth, and said: "You may often need food and not know where to find it. Wherever you spread this, what food you require will be on it."

Although Blaiman, because of his troubles, had no care for anything, he took the cloth with him. He was traveling all day, and at nightfall came to a break in the mountain, a sheltered spot, and he saw remains of a fire.

"I will go no farther tonight," said he.

After a time he pulled out the tablecloth, and food for a king or a champion appeared on it quickly. He was not long eating when a little hound from the break in the mountain came toward him and stood at some distance, being afraid to come near.

"Oh," said the hound, "have you crumbs or burned bread-crusts that you would give me to take to my children, now dying of hunger? For three days I have not been able to hunt food for them."

"I have, of course," said Blaiman. "Come, eat enough of what you like best, and carry away what you can."

"You have my dear love forever," said the hound. "You are not like the thief that was here three nights ago. When I asked him for help, he threw a log of wood at me and broke my shoulder blade, and I have not been able to find food for my little children since that night. Doleful and sad was the lady who was with him; she ate no bite and drank no sup the whole night, but was shedding tears. If ever you are in hardship and need my assistance, call for the Little Hound of Tranamee, and you will have me to help you."

"Stay with me," said Blaiman, "a part of the night; I am lonely, and you may take with you whatever food you can carry."

The hound remained till he thought it time to go home; Blaiman gave him what he could carry, and he was thankful.

Blaiman stayed there till daybreak, spread his cloth again, and ate what he wanted. He was in very good courage from the tidings concerning his wife. He journeyed swiftly all day, thinking he would reach the castle of Hung Up Naked in the evening; but it was still far away.

He came in the evening to a place like that in which he had been the night previous, and thought to himself, "I will stay here tonight." He spread his cloth, and had food for a king or a champion. He was not long eating when there came out opposite him a hawk, and asked:

"Have you crumbs or burned crusts to give me for my little children?"

"Oh," said Blaiman, "come and eat your fill, and take away what you are able to carry."

The hawk ate his fill. "My love to you forever," said the hawk. "This is not how I was treated by the thief who was here three nights ago. When I asked him for food, he flung a log of wood at me and almost broke my wing."

"Give me your company a part of the night; I am lonely," said Blaiman.

The hawk remained with him, and later on added: "The lady who went with the thief was doleful and careworn; she ate nothing, but shed tears all the time."

When going, and Blaiman had given him all the food he could carry, the hawk said: "If ever you need my assistance, you have only to call for the Hawk of Cold Cliff, and I will be with you."

The hawk went away, very thankful, and Blaiman was glad that he had tidings again of his wife. Not much of next day overtook him asleep. He rose, ate his breakfast, and hastened forwards. He was in such courage that he passed a mountain at a leap, a valley at a step, and a broad untilled field at a hop. He journeyed all day till he came to a break in the mountain; there he stopped, and was not long eating from his cloth when an otter came down through the glen, stood before him and asked:

"Will you give me crumbs or burned crusts for my little children?"

Blaiman gave him plenty to eat and all he could carry home.

"My love to you forever," said the otter. "When you need aid, call on the Otter of Frothy Pool, and I will be with you. You are not like the thief who was here three nights ago, having your wife with him. She was melting all night with tears, and neither ate nor drank. You will reach the castle of Hung Up

Naked tomorrow at midday. It whirls around like a millstone, continually, and no one can enter but himself; for the castle is enchanted."

The otter went home. Blaiman reached the castle at midday, and knew the place well, from the words of the otter. He stood looking at the castle; and when the window at which his wife was sitting came before him, she saw him, and, opening the window, made a sign with her hand, and told him to go. She thought that no one could get the upper hand of Hung Up Naked, for the report had gone through the world that no man could kill him.

"I will not go," said Blaiman. "I will not leave you where you are, and now keep the window open."

He stepped back some paces, and went in with one bound through the window when it came around the second time.

While Hung Up Naked was tied to the tree, the tributes of his kingdom remained uncollected; and when he had the woman he wanted safe in his castle, he went to collect the tributes. She had laid an injunction on him to leave her in freedom for a day and a year. She knew when he would be returning, and when that time was near she hid Blaiman.

"Good, good!" cried Hung Up Naked, when he came. "I smell on this little sod of truth that a man from Erin is here."

"How could a man from Erin be here?" asked Blaiman's wife. "The only person from Erin in this is a robin. I threw a fork at him. There is a drop of blood on the fork now; that is what you smell on the little sod."

"That may be," said Hung Up Naked.

Blaiman and the wife were planning to destroy Hung Up Naked, but no one had knowledge how to kill him. At last they made a plan to come at the knowledge.

"It is a wonder," said the woman to Hung Up Naked, "that a great man like yourself should go traveling alone; my father always takes guards with him."

"I need no guards; no one can kill me."

"How is that?"

"Oh, my life is in that block of wood there."

"If it is there, 'tis in a strange place; and it is little trouble you take for it. You should put it in some secure spot in the castle."

"The place is good enough," said he.

When Hung Up Naked went off next day, the wife told Blaiman all she had heard.

"His life is not there," answered Blaiman; "try him again to-night."

She searched the whole castle, and what silk or satin or jewels she found, she dressed with them the block of wood. When Hung Up Naked came home in the evening, and saw the block so richly decked, he laughed heartily.

"Why do you laugh?" asked the woman.

"Out of pity for you. It is not there that my life is at all."

On hearing these words she fainted, was stiff and cold for some time, till he began to fear she was dead.

"What is the matter?" asked Hung Up Naked.

"I did not think you would make sport of me. You know that I love you, and why did you deceive me?"

Hung Up Naked was wonderfully glad. He took her to the window, and, pointing to a large tree growing opposite, asked:

"Do you see that tree?"

"I do."

"Do you see that axe under my bedpost?" He showed the axe. "I cannot be killed till a champion with one blow of that axe splits the tree from the top to the roots of it. Out of the tree a ram will rush forth, and nothing on earth can come up with the ram but the Little Hound of Tranamee. If the ram is caught, he will drop a duck; the duck will fly out on the sea, and nothing on earth can catch that duck but the Hawk of Cold Cliff. If the duck is caught, she will drop an egg into the sea, and nothing on earth can find the egg but the Otter of Frothy Pool. If the egg is found, the champion must strike with one cast of it this dark spot here under by left breast, and strike me through the heart. If the tree were touched, I should feel it, wherever I might be."

He went away next morning. Blaiman took the axe, and with one blow split the tree from top to roots; out rushed the ram. Blaiman rushed after him through the fields. Blaiman hunted the ram till he was dropping from weariness. Only then did he think of the hound, and cry:

"Where are you now, Little Hound of Tranamee?"

"I am here," said the hound, "but I could not come till you called me."

The hound seized the ram in one moment; but, if he did, out sprang a duck, and away she flew over the sea. Blaiman called for the Hawk of Cold Cliff. The hawk caught the duck; the duck dropped an egg. He called the Otter of Frothy Pool; the otter brought the egg in his mouth. Blaiman took the egg and ran to the castle, which was whirling no longer; the enchantment left the place when the tree was split. He opened the door and stood inside, but was not long there when he saw Hung Up Naked coming in haste. When the tree was split, he felt it and hurried home. When he was nearing the castle, his breast open and bare, and he sweating and sweltering, Blaiman aimed at the black spot, and killed Hung Up Naked.

They were all very glad then. The hawk, hound, and otter were delighted; they were three sons of the king of that kingdom which Hung Up Naked had seized; they received their own forms again, and all rejoiced.

Blaiman did not stay long. He left the three brothers in their own castle and kingdom.

"If ever you need my assistance," said Blaiman to the brothers, "send for me at my father-in-law's."

On his return, he spent a night at each place where he had stopped in going.

When the king saw his daughter and Blaiman, he almost dropped dead from joy. They all spent some days very happily. Blaiman now thought of his uncles; and for three days servants were drawing every choice thing to his vessel. His wife went also to the ship. When all was ready, Blaiman remembered a present that he had set aside for his mother, and hurried back to the castle, leaving his wife on the ship with his uncles. The uncles sailed at once for Erin. When Blaiman came back with the present, he found neither wife, ship, nor uncles before him. He ran away like one mad, would not return to his father-in-law, but went wild in the woods, and began to live like the beasts of the wilderness. One time he came out on an edge of the forest, which was on a headland running into the sea, and saw a vessel near land; he was coming that time to his senses, and signaled. The captain saw him and said:

"That must be a wild beast of some kind; hair is growing all over his body. Will some of you go to see what is there? If a man, bring him on board."

Five men rowed to land and hailed Blaiman. He answered, "I am from Erin, and I am perishing here from hunger and cold."

They took him on board. The captain treated him kindly, had his hair cut, and gave him good clothing. Where should the captain be sailing to but the very same port of his grandfather's kingdom from which Blaiman had sailed. There was a high tide when the ship neared, and they never stopped till she was in at the quay. Blaiman went on shore, walked to the chief street, and stood with his back to a house. Soon he saw men and horses carrying and drawing many kinds of provisions, and all going one way.

"Why are these people all going one way?" inquired Blaiman of a man in the crowd.

"You must be a stranger," answered the man, "since you do not know that they are going to the castle. The king's elder son will be married this evening. The bride is the only daughter of the king of the kingdom of the White Strand; they brought her to this place twelve months ago."

"I am a stranger," said Blaiman, "and have only come now from the sea."

"All are invited to the wedding, high and low, rich and poor."

"I will go as well as another," said Blaiman, and he went toward the castle. He met a sturdy old beggar in a long gray coat.

"Will you sell me the coat?" inquired Blaiman.

"Take your joke to some other man," answered the beggar.

"I am not joking," said Blaiman. "I'll buy your coat."

The beggar asked more for the coat than he thought would be given by anyone.

"Here is your money," said Blaiman.

The beggar gave up the coat and started to go in another direction.

"Come back here," said Blaiman. "I will do you more good, and I need your company."

They went toward the castle together. There was a broad space in front of the kitchen filled with poor people, for the greater part beggars, and these were all fighting for places. When Blaiman came, he commanded the crowd to be quiet, and threatened. He soon controlled all, and was himself neither eating nor drinking, but seeing justice done those who were eating and drinking. The servants, astonished that the great, threatening beggar was neither eating nor drinking, gave a great cup of wine to him. He took a good draft of the wine, but left still a fair share in the cup. In this he dropped the ring that he got from his wife in her own father's castle, and said to a servant:

"Put this cup in the hand of the bride, and say: ' 'Tis the big beggar that sends back this much of his wine, and asks you to drink to your own health.' "

She was astonished, and, taking the cup to the window, saw a ring at the bottom. She took the ring, knew it, and ran out wild with delight through the people. All thought 'twas enchantment the beggar had used, but she embraced him and kissed him. The servants surrounded the beggar to seize him. The king's daughter ordered them off and brought him into the castle, and Blaiman locked the doors. The bride then put a girdle around the queen's waist, and this was a girdle of truth. If anyone having it on did not tell the truth, the girdle would shrink and tighten, and squeeze the life out of that person.

"Tell me now," said the bride, "who your elder son's father is."

"Who is he," said the queen, "but the king?"

The girdle grew tighter and tighter till the queen screamed:

"The coachman!"

"Who is the second son's father?"

"The butler."

"Who is your daughter's father?"

"The king."

"I knew," said the bride, "that there was no kingly blood in the veins of the two, from the way that they treated my husband."

She told them all present how the two had taken her away and left her husband behind. When Blaiman's mother saw her son, she dropped almost dead from delight.

The king now commanded his subjects to bring poles and branches and all dry wood, and put down a great fire. The heads and heels of the queen's two sons were tied together, and they were flung in and burned to ashes.

Blaiman remained awhile with his grandfather, and then took his wife back to her father's kingdom, where they lived many years.

The Widow's Son and the Wizard

*T*HERE WAS a woman there long ago and she had only one son. His name was Manus. One day he said to his mother that he would take to the road and seek his fortune. And so he did; he went on his way, and he kept going and going till he came to a crossroads, and whom should he meet there but the wizard.

They saluted one another.

"Would you care to play a game of cards?" asked the wizard.

"Well, indeed, it was not much practice I ever had at cards," said Manus, "but all the same I'll play a game with you."

They played a game then, and Manus won.

"Name your penalty, Manus," said the wizard.

"I place you under a penalty to put the finest mansion that ever was seen in the place of my sooty old cabin that I have as a home."

They played another game, and Manus won again.

"What is your penalty this time, Manus?" asked the wizard.

"I place you under bonds to put a big mill, that will grind every sort of wheat, on the little stream of water at the back of my house."

And so it was. Manus went home, and all was there before him, the big mansion and the mill. One day he went to the crossroads again, and the wizard was there before him.

"Here you are again," said the wizard.

"Here I am," said Manus.

"Will you play a game with me today?" asked the wizard.

"I may as well," said Manus.

So they played again, and Manus won.

"What is your penalty this time?" asked the wizard.

"I put you under bonds to get for me the most beautiful woman in the whole world," said Manus.

"I will get her for you, or you are impossible to please," said the wizard.

He took Manus into a room then, where there were twelve ladies-in-waiting. Their tresses were as red as the fox, and their skin as white as the swan.

"Take your choice, Manus," said the wizard.

"My choice is not among them," said Manus.

He brought him into another room then, where there were twelve dark-haired ladies-in-waiting.

"Take your choice, Manus," said the wizard.

"My choice is not among them," said Manus.

"You are hard to please," said the wizard. He took him then into another room, where there were twelve gray old hags who had never been married.

"Pick your choice, Manus," said the wizard.

"Get along with you, wizard!" said Manus. "No man in the world would marry one of them, if he were never to get a wife."

"It is not in my power to get the woman that will please you," said the wizard. They went out then, and who should be coming down the road but a fine young woman carrying a can of water on her head.

"The woman coming down the road towards us now is the woman I'll have," said Manus.

"My blessing on you, and my curse on the mouth that instructed you," said the wizard.

Manus and the wizard's daughter, as it was she that was there, went home then. They were married shortly after that.

The daughter of the wizard had all the magic that her father knew.

The day after the marriage Manus went to the crossroads again, and the wizard was waiting for him.

"How do you like your bargain, Manus?" he asked him.

"I think it is a good bargain," said Manus.

"Would you like to play another game of cards with me to-day? 'Twill pass a bit of the day for us," said the wizard.

"I don't mind if I do," said Manus.

They played a game then, and the wizard won.

"Name your penalty," said Manus.

"I put you under bonds," said the wizard, "to take the head off my brother in the Eastern World, and to bring it here to me. You must also bring me his cannon gun and his Sword of Light."

"Will you give me respite until tomorrow?" said Manus.

"I will, of course, why wouldn't I," said the wizard.

Manus went home to his wife.

"What news have you today?" asked his wife.

"I have to go a long way from home," said Manus.

"Where have you to go?"

"I have to bring the head of the wizard's brother to him from the Eastern World, his cannon gun and his Sword of Light."

"Very well," said his wife. "When you get up in the morning, take the bridle that you will find hanging behind in the gable. Go to the wizard with it and tell him that you cannot go to the Eastern World unless he will give you a horse to ride. He will say to you that, of course, he will give it to you, and why wouldn't he. He will take you in then to a seven-acre field, and it will be full of the best horses that anyone's eye ever rested on.

And he will tell you take your choice. Draw out that bridle then, and shake it, and do not take any other horse but the one that will come to you and put his head into the bridle."

And that's the way it was; he went to the wizard, and he had the bridle with him. The wizard took him to the place where he had his horses. Manus shook the bridle, and if he had been shaking it ever since, no horse would come to him. I may as well make a long story short. The wizard took him to another place, where he had as many more horses, even finer than those in the first field. Manus shook the bridle, and if he were to be shaking it yet, no horse would come to him. He then took him into another field, a field of ten acres, and it was full of old horses that had been let out to graze there. Manus shook the bridle again, and after waiting for a little while, what should come slowly towards him, and thrust her head into the bridle, but the worst-looking horse that was in the field.

"Oh, confound you!" said Manus. "I suppose if there were one worse than you here, it is he that would come to me."

All the same he mounted her, and as soon as he was on her back, she made off with a bound. They went so quickly that they could keep up with the March wind in front of them, and the March wind behind them could not keep up with them. They would clear twenty-one hills with a leap, and twelve glens with a hop. They never stopped nor stayed till they came up to the domain of the wizard of the Eastern World. The wall was so high that it frightened Manus, and when the little mare took a leap at it, Manus pulled the bridle hard. The little mare said to him:

"If you do that again I will leave you here by yourself, and I will go back home."

Then she made another jump at the wall, and she cleared it

as smoothly as a bird, and she landed in so lightly on the land of the wizard that she would hardly break eggs if they were under her hooves.

So far so good. The mare went on then till she came to a stable; she trotted in, and she told Manus to go and get a riddle of wheat for her. He went and got the riddle of wheat and gave it to the mare, and then he went up to the door of the wizard's palace. He knocked on the door, and out came the wizard himself. Manus was not in dread of him, though he knew that no one ever had stood on the wizard's land that had not been killed by him. The wizard looked at Manus, and was greatly surprised to see there was no sign of fear on him.

"What brought you here?" he asked him. "And who are you?"

"These are things I won't tell you," said Manus.

"Very well," said the wizard. "I'll tell you what we'll do; we'll spend a third of the night talking, a third telling stories, and a third playing tricks on each other. If I beat you at a trick, I will take the head off you, on the spot."

Manus said he was satisfied with that bargain, and asked when they would start the tricks.

The wizard said they would start there and then.

"Let you hide yourself," he said, "and if I find you, I'll take your head and your life."

Manus went out then to the little horse, and he told her that he and the wizard were going to start playing tricks on each other, and that he was going to start:

"I'm to hide myself from him, and if he finds me, I will lose my head."

"Well then," said the mare, "if you do what I will tell you, you will outwit him."

"Tell me, and I will do whatever you say," said Manus.

"I have a toothache," said the mare, "and you must pull out
the tooth for me."

"Confound you, you ugly little mare!" said Manus. "A thing
I never did, even for my own mother, I'm not going to do for
you now."

"If you don't, you'll be sorry," said the horse.

"Well, then I suppose I'd better take your advice," said Manus.
So he put his hand back into her mouth, to pull out the sore
tooth, and the mare drew him back into her mouth and made a
back tooth out of him.

Very soon the wizard was looking for him everywhere, and
he did not leave a place in the seven kingdoms that he did not
search, but no trace of Manus did he find. Then, when the day
came to an end, and the time for searching was over, the little
horse threw Manus out of her mouth, and he was as well and as
healthy as ever he was.

"Now," said she to him, "go in now, and start mocking him
and tell him you were back in the stable all the time."

Manus went into the palace and began mocking the wizard.

"Where were you since morning?" asked the wizard.

"Oh indeed, it was often you passed me by during the day,
and you did not see me. I was at the back of the stable all the
time."

"Well," said the wizard, "I searched every other place except
there."

Next morning Manus brought a riddle of oats out to the little
horse, and told her he was to hide from the wizard again.

"Where will you go this time?" she asked.

"I don't know in the world," he answered.

"There's a gray hair at the end of my tail; pull it out for me,"
she said.

"Well, you ugly little thing," said Manus, "I will not do the like, even for my own mother."

"If you do not do as I tell you, you'll be sorry," said she.

So Manus pulled out the one gray rib of hair, and she made a rib of hair of him. The wizard went off then, and he did not leave a spot in the seven kingdoms that he didn't search for Manus, from top to bottom, and when the day was up he returned home.

The little horse threw Manus off her tail, and he was in his own shape again, as well and as healthy as ever. He went into the palace and began to mock the wizard for not finding him.

"Where were you since morning?" asked the wizard.

"I was at the back of the hayrick, out there in the yard. I don't know how you did not see me. Maybe 'tis going blind you are."

"I searched every place but that," said the wizard.

Next morning Manus went out with a riddle of wheat to the little horse. She spoke to him and said:

"There's a lump in my throat, and I cannot eat the wheat. You ought to stretch your hand back and break the lump."

"You dirty little thing, I'll not be doctoring you," said Manus.

"If you don't do what I'm telling you, you'll be sorry for it," said the little horse.

Manus put his hand back down the horse's throat then, and she drew him back into her stomach entirely. The wizard then went off searching for him in every part of his land, up and down, hither and over, but, of course, there was no Manus to be found anywhere.

"By my word," said he to himself, "I will have lost the game if I do not find him this time, the miserable little worm, wherever he is."

He thought that the little horse had magic and was hiding

Manus, so he did not leave a rib of hair on her hide that he did not tear off, but he failed to find him this time also. When the day was up the little horse threw Manus out of her stomach, and he was as well and as healthy as ever he was.

"Go in now, and mock the wizard again. Ask him if he saw a group of lads playing hurley," said she. "Ask him if he saw one of them settling a dispute among the others, and that he was calling out to him. Tell him that you were that one."

Manus went in then and started making fun of the wizard, more than ever this time:

"What in the world were you doing at all, this day, wizard?"

"Isn't it equal to you? Where were you yourself since morning?"

"I'll tell you then. Maybe you didn't see a crowd of lads playing hurley?"

"I did see them," said the wizard.

"Maybe you didn't see a man who was settling a dispute between them, and he calling out to you?"

"I did indeed," said the wizard.

"Well, it is I that was there."

So far so good. The following morning the wizard started to play his tricks. Manus brought a riddle of wheat out to the little horse.

"I'm in as much danger now as ever I was," he said sadly.

"If you do what I will tell you, you will be all right," said she. "What task has he given you today?"

"Oh," said Manus, "the wizard has gone off, and I do not know, dead or alive, where to find him. If I do not find him before night, he will take the head off me."

"Listen to me now; go in to the servant girl that's inside in the kitchen, and see if you can take off the ring that is on her finger, for that is the wizard."

And signs on, he went in and began to talk to the servant girl.

"That's a nice ring you have on you. Show it to me till I have a look at it."

"It wasn't from Spain it came," she said.

At that he seized her hand and took the ring off her, and he made as if to throw it into the fire.

"Stop! Stop!" said the wizard. "It is I that am here!"

And so the day was won by Manus.

On the following morning he took a riddle of wheat out to the little horse.

"I'm as badly off as ever I was now," said he. "The wizard is gone and I don't know where in the wide world he is."

"You won't be long so," said the little horse. "Go in to the servant girl and start chatting to her. When you will have spent a little while chatting with her, ask her to come out walking in the garden with you. Look out for a tree in the garden that has only one apple on it. Take that apple, for that is the wizard. Get your knife then, and make two halves of it, one for yourself, and one for the servant girl."

Manus went in then and started talking about this and that with the servant girl, and when he had spent a little while talking to her, he asked her to come out walking in the garden. She went out with him. They strolled along until he saw the tree that had only one apple on it. He jumped up and picked the apple. He drew the knife out of his pocket to make two halves of it — half for himself, and half for the girl.

"Stop! Stop!" said the wizard. "It is I that am here."

So Manus won the day.

"I will give you a respite now," said Manus, "a thing you would not do for me, if you had found me. But if I find you the third day, I will take the head off you, and your life with it."

So far so good. On the morning of the third day Manus took a riddle of wheat out to the little horse.

"I am as badly off as ever I was now," said he.

"There is no fear of you, if you do what I am going to tell you."

"What is that?" asked Manus.

"There is," said the little horse, "a tin can inside behind the big door. Go in now to the servant girl and ask her where it is. She won't tell you, for there is a big mouse in under that tin, and that is the wizard. Let you go then and find the big chest that is back in a room behind the house, and you will get the Sword of Light inside in it, and say to the servant girl that if she does not show you the tin can, you yourself will search till you will find it."

He went in then and asked the servant girl where the tin can was. She would not show it to him.

"I will go and find it myself," said he.

"If you do you will be sorry," she told him.

He went in first to the room behind the house where the big chest was, and he found the Sword of Light inside in it. He took it with him and went to look for the tin can. He found it behind the door, and he turned it upside down. Right enough, what should run out of it but a big mouse. He made for it with the sword, to kill it.

"Stop! Stop!" said the wizard. "It is I that am here."

"I don't care if you were there a hundred times, I've given you plenty of chances already, what you wouldn't give me." So he drew his sword back and swept the head off the wizard.

"If I can get on my own body again," said the head, "half the Fianna of Erin will not be able to behead me again."

"That's a chance you'll never get," said Manus, "for I want your head."

The head then started to jump around the floor, and Manus drew another blow at it with the sword. He put it under his arm then and took it off with him.

So far so good. He took a riddle of wheat to the little horse, and when she saw the head, she said:

"What's that you have there?"

"That's the head of the wizard. I have the Sword of Light too — more than half of what I was sent for."

"What else were you sent for?" she asked.

"The cannon gun," said Manus.

"I will tell you now where you will come by that," said the little horse. "There's a big heap of lime out there in the stable yard. Let you go out to it, and dig around a bit, and you will find a mattock. Take that mattock with you, and lay it down on the flagstone that is out opposite the big door of the palace, and the flagstone will rise up of itself. The cannon gun is under that."

Out went Manus. He dug up the heap of lime, and he found the mattock. He went over to the big door then and he laid the mattock down on the flagstone that was in front of it, and the flagstone rose up on the spot. He found the cannon gun under it. He took the cannon gun then, and the Sword of Light and the head of the wizard, and made back to the little horse.

"You have them all now," said the little horse.

"I have indeed, and my seven blessings on you, because only for you, I would have been dead long ago," said Manus. "We'll start out for home tomorrow, so let you be ready."

"I will indeed, I'll be ready in the morning when you will come out to me."

Early next morning he went out to her with the riddle of

wheat as he had done every morning while they were in the Eastern World. When she had eaten the wheat she said to him: "Get up on my back now, and do not draw a tight rein on me till we reach the other wizard in the Western World."

Manus mounted on the little horse then, carrying the head of the wizard, the Sword of Light and the cannon gun. Off with them then, and they went so quickly that they would catch up with the March wind in front of them, and the March wind that was behind them could not catch up with them. As short a time as they took going, they took shorter coming back, and it wasn't long till they landed back in the domain of the first wizard.

"Now," said the little horse, "go in to the wizard. When he will see you, he will try to get the Sword of Light from you first, but for the life of you do not give it to him. If you do, he will sweep the head off you with it. Tell him you will not give it to him, but that you will have the same contest with him as you had with the wizard of the Eastern World. He will attack you then, and he will try to take the cannon gun and the Sword of Light from you. Strike the head off him with the Sword of Light, or he will take your head."

"I will do that," said Manus.

He went in then, and the wizard came to the door to him.

"A hundred thousand welcomes, Manus," said he. "Have you got those things I sent you for?"

"I have," said Manus, throwing the head of the other wizard before him. "There is one of them for you."

"Give me the Sword of Light," said the wizard, and anger was shining in his eyes.

"Ha! How unmannerly you are! Don't you think that I deserve to have it more than you, since it was I who went for it?"

"That does not matter," said the wizard; "you will have to give them to me now, or I will take your head and your life along with them."

"If that's the way you want it," said Manus, "I'll do the same to you as I did to your brother. Look out for yourself."

But the words weren't out of his mouth when the wizard made for him, and Manus gave one thrust with the Sword of Light, and swept the head off him, and when it fell to the ground he made two halves of it. Immediately he did this, the wizard fell down in a heap of jelly.

Good enough! Manus had killed the wizard, or so he thought. Off with him then to the little horse.

"How did you get on, Manus?" she asked.

"I have killed the wizard, in spite of all his magic. But that is thanks to you."

"That's a good job done," said the little horse. "You won't see a poor day now, from this on, as long as you feed me."

"You well deserve the feeding," said Manus. "But now it may be as well for me to pay a visit to my wife and my mother. Be ready to set out again in the morning."

Manus went out in the morning, and he took a riddle of wheat to the little horse. When she had eaten it, he mounted her, and they set off for the castle of Manus. When he arrived there, he rode straight to the stableyard and put her into a stable. He went then and knocked on the castle door. His wife came out and welcomed him.

"A hundred welcomes home before you, Manus," said she. "How did you get on in your travels?"

"Very well," said Manus. "I have riches enough now to last me as long as I live. I have killed the wizard."

"If you have killed him, you'll never see a poor day again," said she.

So far so good. Time went by, and Manus was doing well. He had the little horse, he was grinding every kind of grain in the mill, and he and his wife and his mother were living in the fine castle. He bought a carriage, and the three of them used to go out driving in it every day. Everything was going well till the people began mocking the little old horse that Manus had under the carriage.

One day Manus said to his wife: "People are mocking and jeering at the little old horse I have. But they won't be doing that much longer, for I will sell her at the next fair, even if I get only the price of a drink for her."

"If you sell her," said his wife, "you won't have a day's luck as long as you live. The two wizards will come to life again, and they will knock down everything you have."

"I don't care," said Manus.

He went off to the next fair with the little horse, but he got no bid for her till he was going out the tollgates in the evening, when the fair was over, and he was going home for himself. Just by the tollgates, a little man came up to him and said to him:

"How much are you asking for the little horse?"

"I'm not asking much," said Manus. "If I got the price of the two drinks for her, I'd sell her."

"I'll give you that much," said the little old man.

He sold her then, and went back into the fairground, and drank her price in a drinking booth. He took too much drink, and when he began to walk home he was taking the two sides of the road.

When he awoke in the morning Manus hadn't a shred left of castle, carriage, mill or wife. There was nothing left to him but the little old sooty cottage, and his mother sitting in the chimney corner as she always used to be.

"Things are as bad as they can be," said he to himself, "and I won't stay here."

He told his mother that he would go off again. "As I went the first day that I played cards with the wizard."

"Oh, indeed," said his mother to him, "when you went before the wizard put his bad mark on you; it would be better for you to stay at home and have sense."

"I don't care a straw," said he.

He went off then, and he left his poor old mother in the smoky cabin after him. He walked on and on, until the night was gaining on the day. And then, what should he see fighting inside a wall, but a hawk, an otter and a fox. He thought it would be a good thing to settle whatever dispute there was between them. He went over the wall to them, and he made three parts of an old sheep that was thrown there against the wall. He gave a third of it to the hawk of the cold, windy cliffs, a third to the otter of the big river, and a third of it to the fox of the furze bushes.

"If you ever need help from a hawk of the cold, windy cliffs, call on me," said the hawk.

"If ever you need an otter from the big river," said the otter, "call on me."

"If ever you need a swift fox of the furzy slopes, call on me," said the fox.

He went on then till he saw a light, and he went towards it. He came to a house where he got lodging for the night. In the morning he bade "Good morning" to a man that was there, and he asked him:

"Is there a house near this place?"

"There is a wizard living in a castle four miles away, and no one ever put his foot inside it that the wizard did not kill."

"I do not mind that," said Manus. "I'll go and have a look at him."

He went on then and he never stopped until he came to the castle of the wizard. The wizard was away from home, with his brother in the Eastern World. Manus went in, and he bade "Good morrow" to the servant girl.

"Would you give me a bite to eat, if you please?" he asked her.

"Fear would not let me," she said, "for if the wizard saw anyone like you here, he would kill you, and me along with you."

"Give me shelter for the night anyway — death comes only once to everyone."

"I don't know in the world where I will put you," said she, "unless you'll sleep in that vat behind the stable, and maybe if you went well in under it, he wouldn't see you."

"I'll do that," said Manus.

He went under the vat then, and he had only just done so when the wizard and his followers came back. As soon as he had landed on his own domain — the Island of Magic — he got the smell of an Irishman, and he asked the servant girl had any strange man or woman come into his territory while he was away.

"No," said the servant girl, "but a man passed by this morning, searching for you, to put you to death."

"Oho," said the wizard, "there isn't a man living who could put me to death."

"Why not?" asked the girl.

"Do you see that tree outside there?" asked the wizard.

"I do," said the girl.

"That it may last a long time!" said the wizard. "There is a hare inside in the middle of that tree, and there's a wild duck inside in the stomach of the hare; and until the egg that is in that wild duck's belly is thrown at my forehead, there is no killing me."

So far so good. The wizard went away the following day to the Eastern World, and when he was gone, the servant girl went out to Manus, and brought him in, and gave him a good meal.

"Now," she said to him, as soon as he had eaten the food, "if you do everything I tell you, we will be able to kill the wizard."

"Tell me," he said.

"Do you see that tree outside there? Well, there's a hare in the middle of that tree, and there's a wild duck in his stomach, and an egg in the stomach of the wild duck. If you can get that egg, and throw it at the forehead of the wizard, you will kill him."

"By my troth," said Manus, "if that's the case, he won't be long alive. Have you an axe? If you have, give it to me now."

She gave him the axe, an axe made of gold it was, and out with him quickly. He had only to strike one single blow of that axe on the tree when it fell down to the ground. Out rushed the hare.

"Hulloo, hulloo!" said the girl. "There's the hare out! He's gone off! We're as badly off now as ever we were, and worse, for the wizard will kill us."

"Help, help, swift fox of the furzy slopes!" said Manus.

The words were hardly out of his mouth when the fox was after the hare, neck and neck. She caught him in no time and took a bite out of his stomach.

"Oh, there goes the wild duck," said the servant girl. "We're finished now altogether!"

"Help, help, hawk of the cold cliffs!" cried Manus.

The words were hardly out of his mouth when the hawk appeared up in the sky, like a flash of lightning. He took a few turns out of the wild duck, they were out over the sea by this, then he made a swoop down on her and made a hole in her belly. The egg fell out and dropped down into the sea.

"Oh horror of horrors! We're now in a worse plight than ever," said the servant girl.

"Help, help, O otter from the big river!" cried Manus.

The words were hardly out of his mouth when the otter came up out of the sea, carrying the egg in his mouth.

"Good fortune is with us this time," said the girl, "and the wizard's day is done."

Home with them then, as quickly as they could go, taking the egg along with them. When they reached the wizard's castle, the girl said to Manus:

"Go out now, and you will find that the little horse is outside in the stable; bring her around here, and you and I will leave the Island of Magic before the wizard comes home. I'm your own wife, Manus, though you never once recognized me."

"Surely it isn't possible that you are my lost wife?" said Manus.

"There is not a doubt in the world but that 'tis true, and I will never be parted from you again. But make haste and go out for the little horse, or the wizard will be back before you are ready."

Manus went out, and he was well delighted with himself, and what should he find in the stable before him but the little mare that he had sold.

"By my sowl, is it you that are there?" said he to her, and he was full of joy at seeing her again. He put the bridle on her then, and he took her out of the stable with him. He mounted her, and he put his wife up behind him. Off with them then, taking the wild duck's egg with them, and the March wind that was behind them could not catch up with them. When they had gone a hundred miles they looked back, and what did they see coming after them but the wizard, his mouth frothing and two horns out of his head.

"O Manus dear, he is coming! Are you a good shot?" asked his wife.

"I'm a fair shot, but maybe you're a better one," said he.

"There's no time to waste," said she. "Keep on going, and I'll turn around and face the wizard."

The wizard was drawing up to them all the time, and when he was within firing distance of her, she threw the egg. It hit him fair in the middle of the forehead. She put half of him in the Eastern World and half of him in the Western World, and all his fighting gear and weapons fell to the ground.

Manus and his wife started off again quicker than ever. They took twenty-one hills with a hop, and twelve glens with a leap, and soon they reached home. The castle of Manus was once more standing before them, and the mill was grinding away, as it used to be whenever he came home before. He and his wife and his mother had full and plenty, as long as they lived from that on, and believe me, he did not sell the little horse again.

Liam Donn

LIAM DONN was the son of the High King of Ireland. One day the High King was out hunting on a hilltop. He saw a wild duck in the glen with twelve ducklings after her, and they were making towards the lake. It was not long till he noticed that the duck was attacking one of her brood, and driving him off from the others. He saw the duckling come back after a while and join up with the rest, and he saw the mother attacking him again and driving him off once more, pecking him with her beak and flapping her wings at him. For the third time the duckling got up and followed the brood, and for the third time the mother drove him away. The High King thought that it was a strange thing for the mother duck to peck and drive off her own nestling as she did, and he went to the Wise Old Man to get the meaning of it.

"The wild duck laid twelve eggs, she hatched the twelve eggs, and she brought out twelve birds," said the Wise Old Man, "and now one of the ducklings was given to the *Deachma* [tithe]. So the bird you saw her driving off, she was giving to the *Deachma*. For neither she nor her brood would have any luck if they did not give one duckling to the *Deachma*."

"Well," said the High King, "I have twelve sons, and how do I know if it would not be right for me to give one to the *Deachma* too?"

"You can never have any luck till you give one to the *Deachma* too," said the Wise Old Man.

The High King came home and told the story to his wife. Neither he nor she knew which of their sons they should send away. That day all the children were out hunting, and the High King and his wife made up their minds to send away whichever of the sons was the last to come in from the hunt.

They went out to the gate then to wait for their sons coming home. It so happened that the youngest son, Liam Donn, was the last to come back, and the father shut the gate against him. The king and the queen had not as much affection for any of their children as they had for Liam Donn, the youngest, and their hearts were broken when they saw that he was the last one home, but they could not break their word.

All the same they did not drive him off the first day.

"Of all the sons in my house, you are the one I think worst of losing, Liam Donn," said the king to his son, "so I will give you one day's respite."

On the following day the sons went hunting again, and it was Liam who was last coming home this time too, but still the king's heart would not let him banish him, and he gave him respite for a second day. On the third day it happened just as on the two other days, Liam Donn was the last coming home again, and though the king's heart was breaking, he closed the gate against him.

"I think, son," said the king, "that you are the son of the *Deachma,* and that you are the one to be banished; and now, though you are as dear to me as the sight of my two eyes, I must send you out on the roads of the world. The King of Greece has twelve daughters and her father has just given one of them to the *Deachma,* and she has been sent off on the roads of the world, as we are sending you now. Bright Hands is the

LIAM DONN

name of the daughter that the King of Greece has given to the *Deachma*, but Una of the *Deachma* is the name she goes by since she was banished from home. Now you must go and look for tidings of Una of the *Deachma*, and do not ever come back here to me till you find her, and until you rescue her."

"I must go and see my mother and get her blessing before I go off looking for anyone," said Liam Donn. He made a running leap at the palisade and he cleared it in a jump. He went into his father's house and he sat down on a hard chair. He gave a sigh and his breast swelled so much that the ribs broke the hard knot of jealousy in his breast and the sigh broke the hard chair under him, so that it fell on the granite flagstones of the hearth.

"I bless and praise you, son," said his mother, "and it is a sorrowful thing that we have to part with you, for you are the makings of a better warrior than any of our other sons."

She made three cakes then, one with breast milk, one with beef blood and another out of bee's beer, and she cooked them. When Liam Donn was saying goodbye, his mother gave him the three cakes with her blessing, and she told him that there was victory in each one of the cakes, and that anyone that would be hit by one of them would be killed.

Liam Donn then said goodbye to his people, and he made off for the big road to look for tidings of Una of the *Deachma*, or Bright Hands, the daughter of the King of Greece. He kept walking all day, and at nightfall he saw a house below him in a lonely glen. He went towards the house. When he went in he saw a young girl opposite a mirror, and she was combing her hair with a golden comb and a silver rack. There was a golden fillet on her forehead and it sparkled in the darkness, and there was another fillet on the back of her head.

"Good morrow to you, young girl," said he.

She answered him in the same words.

"Ah," said she then, "go away from here quickly; the giant will be coming in in ten minutes, and if you are here before him, he will devour you."

"Maybe 'tis less than that he will be able to do to me," said Liam Donn, "and I'm hanged if I'll run away from him."

The giant came in then.

"Fee, fo, fum," said he. "I smell the blood of a base, lying Irishman. You are too big for one mouthful, and too little for two mouthfuls. I don't know whether I'll put you to boil in the caldron, or whether I'll make a bit of snuff out of you between my five fingers."

"That you may be seven times worse than ever you were, you rascal," said Liam Donn. "Let us have a trial of strength now, before you make either out of me."

They attacked each other then, fiercely and violently, and they stayed fighting each other till both of them were worn out and exhausted. Liam Donn was getting the worst of it when he remembered his mother's cakes. Then he took one of them, and hit the giant with it, fair in the middle of his breast, and he split his carcass. As the giant was falling he took hold of the cake, and ate a mouthful of it. As soon as he tasted the cake he spoke to Liam Donn in a friendly way.

"I bless and hail you, son of my sister! I am well acquainted with the taste of that cake, and it was my sister, your mother, who made it. Anything at all you want I'll give you now, if you will leave a bit of that cake on my wound to heal it."

"I want nothing except to find out from you where in Greece is Una of the *Deachma* to be found."

"I cannot give you that information, Liam Donn," said the giant. "But there are two brothers of mine living between here and Greece, and if you go to them maybe they will be able to answer your question. Here is a red bridle for you, let you

go out to the door of the stable and shake it. A horse that is
the same color as the bridle will come towards you. That horse
will take you to my brothers."

Liam Donn did as the giant told him. He took the horse that
was the same color as the red bridle, and he made off. As the
dusk of the night was gathering he reached the house of the second giant. There was a young woman hostage inside before him,
and she was combing her hair with a golden comb and a silver
rack, as was the young maiden in the house of the first giant. He
saluted the young woman and she answered him in the same
words. She told him then to take himself off quickly, if he
would heed a word of advice, for there was no knowing what
death he would get if the giant came home and found him
there. As they were talking the giant came in, and he was in a
state of wild rage.

"Fee, faw, fum," said as he came through the door. "I smell
the blood of a base, lying Irishman. I don't know whether I will
tear you with my long, cold teeth, or whether I'll put you to
boil in the caldron."

"Do not say that you will do either of them until you will
find out if you will be able," said Liam Donn.

They went for each other quickly and fiercely then, and when
he was getting tired, Liam Donn remembered his mother's cake.
He seized it, and he struck the giant with it, between the mouth
and eyes, and he cracked his skull.

The giant managed to take a bite out of the cake, and the
minute he touched it he recognized his sister's baking.

"I hail you and bless you, child of my sister," said the giant.
"You may have anything you ask now, but first heal my
wounds."

Liam Donn rubbed the cake to the giant's wound and it was
cured on the spot. Then Liam Donn asked him for news of

Una of the *Deachma*. The giant had no tidings of her, but he
gave Liam Donn a steed, the color of hay, and he directed him to
the house of his brother.

Liam Donn said farewell to this giant and he took with him
the hay-colored steed, and went on his journey. In the failing
light of the evening he came to the house of the third giant.
There was a woman hostage inside, with her shining hair flowing around her shoulders while she combed it with a golden
comb and a silver rack. She had a golden fillet on her forehead
and it was glittering in the darkness, and there was another
fillet on the back of her head. Liam Donn saluted her in a
friendly way, and she answered in the same manner.

"O fine strapping youth," said the young woman to Liam
Donn, "get out of here quickly, for the giant is coming, and if
he finds you here before him there is no knowing what death
he will give you."

"I never retreated before anyone yet," said Liam Donn, "and I
won't retreat now. And maybe 'tis less than that he will be
able to do to me."

As they were talking Liam Donn heard a noise like snorting
and grunting coming closer. He peeped out and he saw the
big giant coming at his best and with a fierce devilish look on
his face. He was taking a hill with a hop, two hills with a leap
and passing over a glen with a step. He had five heads, five crops
of hair and five necks on him, a withered tree stump over his
shoulder and a wicker basket, full to the brim with five hundred
bodies, on his arm. He was the most frightful beast Liam Donn
ever saw in his whole life and, as brave as he was, he became a
little afraid of him.

"Fee, faw, fum," said the giant, as he came in the door. "I
smell the blood of a base, lying Irishman. I don't know
whether I'll send you with a puff to the Eastern World, or

with two puffs to the Western World. You are too big for one
mouthful and too small for two."

"Take it easy, rascal," said Liam Donn. "We'll have a contest
before you will do anything with me."

They went for each other then, as would two whirlpools in
an eddy, two calves to the suckling or two warriors to a fight.
They kept fighting each other till they made hard places soft,
and soft places hard, and until they were drawing wells of spring
water up through the gray stones.

After fighting like this for a long time without either of them
getting the upper hand of the other, Liam Donn put forth all
his energy and charged the giant, and with whatever twist he
gave him he put him on his knees on the gray stones, with
the second twist he put him down to his waist, and with the
third, down to his eyelids.

"By my word," said Liam Donn, "if I ever took my mother's
advice, I will take it now," and with that he took the last cake
he had and he hit the giant across the mouth with it. The giant
managed to take a mouthful of the cake before it fell to the
ground.

"I am your friend and your protector, O son of my sister,"
said the giant. "Grant me my life and I will give you anything
you want."

"I will give you that," said Liam Donn, "when you tell me
in what part of Greece does Una of the *Deachma* live, and
what danger she is in that she is in need of rescue."

"I will tell you that and welcome," said the giant, "when you
will free me from my bonds."

Liam Donn then caught a grip of the giant's hair and drew him
up out of the gray stones where he was stuck.

The giant gave a full account to Liam Donn of Una of the
Deachma. He told him she lived on the farther side of the River

of Greece. He told him also that the people of Greece were brokenhearted with sorrow that night, as Una of the *Deachma,* or Bright Hands, daughter of the king, was being sent away from home on the following day, and that a great sea serpent was coming to devour her.

The giant begged and implored Liam Donn to spend that night in his company, and so he did. They made three parts of the night — a third of it telling stories, a third telling Fenian romances and a third eating and drinking. Every morsel was as sweet as honey, and not a single morsel was dry or tasteless, and the tables and benches were laden with the choicest of Danish meats. Then they went to bed and had a deep restful sleep till the following morning.

At the first light of day Liam Donn got up, and he togged himself out in his warrior's clothes. The giant got up too and got the breakfast ready for him. He gave him directions to the road for the River of Greece. He told him there were three hills in his way — a hill of steel needles, a mountain of flame and a mountain of fierce mastiffs, and when he was setting out he gave him a present of a steed and a saddle. Liam Donn then bade farewell to the giant, and he and his mouse-colored steed headed for the River of Greece, where Una of the *Deachma,* daughter of the King of Greece, was.

He came up to the first hill, the hill of the hard steel needles. At the foot of the hill he gave spurs to his steed, and, with a fine agile leap, she cleared the hill with him. They went on then, and it was not long till they came to the second hill — the mountain of flame, where there were flames coming down and flames going up, and flames in between. With the quickness of light they cleared that hill also, and there was only one hill before them now — the hill of the fierce mastiffs. When they were at the bottom of that hill Liam Donn gave spurs to his steed again, she rose up from a spot of level ground, lightly and nimbly, and she cleared the hill with ease. But when the steed was coming down the other side of the hill, one of the fierce mastiffs caught her by the hock and put a spear-like tooth into it. The steed gave a screech out of her when she felt the stab, but if she did it wasn't long until she was cured, for Liam Donn had a little bottle of healing water in his pocket, and before the steed was on the ground, Liam Donn put his hand under her hock and put the healing water on the wound, and she was cured on the spot. The most troublesome part of the journey was past now, and they headed straight for the River of Greece. They came to the river and, after a good sprightly jump, they landed on the other side. They had reached the end of their journey safely.

There was no time for Liam Donn to take a rest, as it was drawing on to twelve o'clock, the hour when the serpent was to come to swallow Una of the *Deachma*. So he rode off quickly to the strand, and there he saw Una of the *Deachma* tied to a rock with heavy chains, waiting for the serpent to come and swallow her.

He spoke gently and civilly to the young woman, but she was sad and gloomy and she paid little heed to his talk.

"Don't be sorrowful, young girl," he said. "I have come here today to save you, if it can be done, by killing the serpent. I came every step of the way from Erin to rescue you."

She did not pay much attention to what he said, because she believed that there was not a warrior in the world could kill the serpent. He sat down by her side and he told her not to let him fall asleep till the serpent came. It was not long till she saw the sea flowing up over the grass, and she told him that the serpent was coming. He went down then to the edge of the sea, and when the serpent came in he attacked it fiercely. He and the serpent stayed fighting each other till the day ended, and at the fall of night, with whatever blow the warrior gave her, he took half the side of the face off the serpent, and on losing her cheek the serpent turned and went away out to sea.

On the following morning Liam Donn came on the strand in his warrior's gear again, and when the serpent came in he attacked her fiercely, and they stayed fighting each other from dawn till sunset. At the first fading of the day he made a slash at her, and took the other cheek off her, and on losing that she made out to sea again.

On the morning after that, when Liam Donn came to the beach, the place was full of people. For the news had spread around the country that a warrior had come to fight the serpent, and that he had saved Una of the *Deachma* from her on the day before. And now they were gathering to see the fight between them.

The serpent came in from the sea once more and Liam Donn went down to meet her. The fight began again, and he was there hacking and striking at her till the setting of the sun. And just as the sun was going down, Liam Donn drew his sword well back behind his shoulder, and with all the strength he could muster, he struck the serpent near the mouth, across the jaw and the neck, and with that blow he took the head off her. That put an end to the serpent, and it was great praise that the people of Greece gave to the brave warrior who had rescued Una of the *Deachma* from the awful death that had been destined for her.

The people tried to keep Liam Donn with them and to take him to the king's court, but he went away from them. As he was riding past the young maiden she seized one of his shoes and brought it home with her. The people then went to the king's court with Una of the *Deachma,* and all passed a happy night, with gaiety and pleasure and joy without stint in the court of the King of Greece, because the serpent had been killed and Bright Hands had been saved from death.

Bright Hands then said that she would never marry anyone but the man that the shoe would fit, so soldiers were sent out with it to find the one who owned it, and there were many who had large feet and who cut off their toes trying to get the shoe on. The soldiers at last came to the place where Liam Donn was, and he had to try on the shoe as well as others, and his foot slipped into it and he was taken to the king's court. Great was the delight of the King of Greece when the warrior was brought before him, and Liam Donn and Bright Hands were married there and then. There was a feast lasting seven days and seven nights, with goblets of honey to drink and the taste of honey on every mouthful, and no mouthful dry or tasteless.

After the wedding Liam Donn came back to Erin, and he brought Una of the *Deachma* along with him. If he had been given a welcome by the King of Greece for the rescuing of Bright Hands, the welcome his father and his own people gave him was seven times greater still. A feast was prepared for him that lasted seven nights and seven days. Tables were laden with the choicest of food and goblets of honey to drink; meats were torn by strong teeth and the bones were chewed by throngs of dogs.

I and my people were there. They went by the ford and I went by the little lake. They were drowned but I came safe. If I have it today, may you not have it tomorrow night, but even so, may you not lose by it but your back teeth.

The Treacherous Eagle

T HERE WAS a king in Ireland one time and he had only one son.
One morning when the servant boys got up they found that the
haggard was full of strange-looking birds. They sent word to the
king and told him about the birds. The king said not to bother
with them till he got up himself, so they paid no more heed to
them.

The king's son was asleep and the talk wakened him. He got
up, put on his clothes and looked out through the window.
When he saw all the queer birds in the haggard he ran for his
gun, fired a shot and wounded an eagle in the leg.

When his father got up later on and saw that the eagle was
lame he asked him what was the cause of his lameness and if
he could get any cure for him.

"It was your son who wounded me," said the eagle," and
nothing will cure me except the seven beeves of the seven years."

"It isn't much you are asking," said the king, "and I will get
them for you whenever you want them."

Then the eagle told everyone who was in the courtyard to
leave, except the king's son. They all left the yard, and when
they had gone the eagle told the king's son to get up on his
back. The king's son did as the eagle told him, but if he did he
couldn't get down again, for the eagle rose up in the air with

him and made off for the Western World. The eagle was the
son of an old witch.

When he reached one of her dwellings he came down. He
told his mother that his leg was wounded but that he had the rascal who had wounded him.

By this time the king and all his court were waiting for the
eagle to come back with his son. But as night came on and they
began to shake with the cold they went inside to wait, but, good
nor bad, there was no trace of the eagle or the boy coming
back.

The old witch told her servant girl to send the king's son
to bed and she gave her a drink of thin beer to give him. The
servant girl sent the king's son to bed, but it wasn't in the
bed that the witch had ordered for him. Instead she made up
a fine comfortable bed for him. She told him then that the
witch was going to give him three difficult tasks to perform,
tasks that no one could succeed in doing, but that she herself
would give him every help and succor, and that he was not to
be dispirited or downcast.

On the following morning after he had got up, the old hag
said to the king's son that he was to drain the lake that was at
the end of the yard, and that he was to find the gold ring that
her grandmother had lost there seven hundred years ago, and
that he was to have it for her before the sun sank into the sea in
the evening. She gave him a cup to bail the water with.

He went off and began trying to bail out the lake, but if he did
it was useless work, for as soon as he threw one cupful out seven
cupfuls would flow in. He sat down for himself after a while,
which was just as good for him, and he stayed sitting there
till the servant girl came out with his dinner. Before he had
finished eating the food, she had drained the lake and had got
the ring.

THE TREACHEROUS EAGLE

"Here is the ring for you now," she said to him, "and keep it safely, for maybe you will have need of it later on."

The girl went away with herself then, and he stayed where he was until late in the evening, when he went back and told the hag that he had found the ring. The hag did not ask him for the ring however, and that made him very pleased.

When he was going to bed the hag told the servant girl to bring him the drink of thin beer, as she had done the first night. But such a thing was far from her mind. Instead she prepared a grand supper with all kinds of dainties for him, and after eating it he went to bed.

On the following morning when he got up, the old hag gave him a three-pronged fork and she told him to clean out a stable where there had been seven hundred horses for seven hundred years and to find a needle that her great-great-grandmother had lost there.

He went to the stable and started throwing out the manure quickly, but if he did his work was in vain for as soon as he would throw out one forkful seven forkfuls would be thrown back in against him, and that went on till the servant girl came with his food. While he was eating the food, she cleaned out the stable and found the needle that had been missing for seven hundred years. She gave the needle to the king's son and she told him to keep it himself and not to give it to the old hag.

The girl went back home then and she never pretended one word to anyone of what she had done. Late in the evening the king's son from Ireland came in and he told the hag that he had found the needle. The hag was sitting on her haunches beside the fire and she never said a word, and that was the way the king's son wished it to be.

When the time for going to bed came, she called out peevishly to the servant girl, and told her to give the drink of thin beer

to the king's son and to go to bed quickly. But not a drop of the
beer did he put near his lips, for instead she had a fine supper
ready for him with all kinds of dainties. After that he went to
bed and she herself went to sleep on a bed she had made ready
for herself on the floor.

On the morning of the third day the old hag handed the
king's son a hatchet, and she took him over to the door and
she showed him a high, broad tree that was growing out before
it. She told him to cut down that tree and to find a box
that was on top of it. There was a duck hatching on one egg in
the box, and she told him he was to get that egg and have it for
her by evening.

He made off then for the tree. He raised the hatchet high
over his head, he hit the trunk of the tree a strong blow, and
sank the axe to its butt. He pulled it out to give another blow,
and a torrent of blood gushed out of the tree so quickly that in
no time a lake of blood formed around him. The king's son had
to flee as the lake went on getting broader and broader. The
servant girl then came with his food, and while he was eating
it she cut down the tree herself. When the tree fell the duck
flew off and the egg fell into the lake of blood, and the courage
of the king's son fell along with it, for he thought that it was
all up with him now. But the girl turned herself into an otter,
and in the twinkling of an eye she brought the egg up from the
bottom of the lake. She told the king's son to keep it safely
along with the ring and the needle.

The girl went off then and the king's son stayed where he was.
When evening drew on he went to the hag and he told her
that he had got the egg. He never said another word then, and
she pretended she had not heard what he had said to her. When
it was time to go to bed the hag told the servant girl to give the
king's son a drink of thin beer, and to go to bed herself after

that But neither of them went to bed but stayed up roasting and boiling and baking food for themselves on the journey they were going to make that night back to Erin.

Three times during the night the hag asked them if they had gone to bed yet. The first time they answered her they said they hadn't gone yet. The second answer they gave her was that they were just going. And the third time she asked she asked she got no answer, for the girl and the king's son had flown off in the shape of two hawks.

They went on then flying until the girl told the king's son to look back and see if there was anyone following them. He looked back and said:

"I see two shapes as small as birds coming after us but they are a great way behind."

"Look back again," said the girl.

"They are like two cocks of hay now," said the king's son.

"That's the hag and her son following us," said the girl.

"They are like two mountains now," said the king's son, looking back once more.

"Throw the ring behind you now," said the girl.

The moment he threw the ring the whole countryside behind them flooded into a great broad lake. Neither the hag nor her son could cross it.

The hag said to her son: "Go home for the big bucket that stands at my door to bail off the lake."

He went back and brought the bucket. They bailed out the lake and the two hastened on.

The girl said to the king's son: "Look behind you now, and see if they are coming."

"They are coming behind us and they look like two birds."

"Look a second time," said the girl.

"They are like two cocks of hay now," said the king's son.

"Look a third time."

"They are like two mountains now," said he.

"Throw the needle behind you now," said the girl.

He threw it behind him, and that moment the whole countryside was covered with enormous steel spikes, standing up like a dense branchless forest before the hag and her son.

"Hurry back home," said the hag to her son, "for the hammer I left after me under the bed."

Off he went and he was soon back with the great heavy hammer. He battered and broke his way through the steel spikes and he and the hag went on again.

Soon the girl said to the king's son, "Look behind and see if they are coming."

"I see only one shape, as large as a bird, coming after us now."

"That's the hàg herself coming after us," said the girl; "the son is tired. Take out the egg now quickly, and if you were ever a good shot, now is the time to prove it. Aim at her breast. If you do not hit it we are both in the pen of death."

When the hag drew near them the king's son threw the egg at her. He aimed it at her left breast as the servant girl had told him. The narrow end of the egg went straight into the witch and the broad end of it followed. Blood poured out of her in a stream, and after a while the life went out of her.

The girl and the king's son went on then to the Western World and to the court of his father in Erin. When they came to court at last the girl told him to go in and that she would wait for him outside.

"I will not go in with you yet," she said, "but promise me that you will not kiss anyone, nor let anyone kiss you, for if you do, you will lose all memory of me from that moment."

He left her then unwillingly, and went in by himself. His fa-

ther and the people of the court all gave him a great welcome,
and he took care not to kiss anybody, or to let anybody kiss him.
His old hunting dog, who was sitting by the fire, jumped up with
joy to welcome him and licked his face. From that moment
he lost all memory of the girl outside waiting for him, just as she
said he would.

Having grown tired of waiting for the king's son, the girl
went off walking along the road until the evening came and the
dew began to fall. She went up in a willow tree then and
settled herself on a branch for the night. There was a river flowing underneath the tree and the moon was shining brightly up
in the sky over her head.

A little distance away there was a smith's forge. During the
night the smith grew thirsty and he told his daughter to go
out to the river and bring him in a pitcher of water to drink.
She took the pitcher and she went to the river. As she bent
down to fill the jug she saw the reflection of the beautiful
girl in the moonlit water, and she thought it was her own reflection. Instead of filling the pitcher she dashed it away from
her angrily, saying that a woman so beautiful shouldn't be
drawing water for an ugly smith. She went off and was seen no
more by the blacksmith. When she did not return he sent another of his daughters out for water, but it was the same
story with her. Then he sent his wife out for the water, but
she was seven times more angry than either of her two daughters when she saw her beautiful face in the water.

"It is a shame for me to be the wife and the slave of a blacksmith, and I such a fine-looking woman!" said she. So she ran
away and never went home to her husband.

The smith was sorely thirsty by this time, so he went out
himself to get the water, in the heel of the hunt. He saw the

reflection in the pool of the river, and he knew well that it was a woman, and he looked up into the tree and saw the girl.

"You have been making fun of the lot of us," said the smith.

"Maybe I have," said the girl.

"Come down now and keep my house for me," said the smith, "because it was on account of you that my wife and daughters have gone off."

She came down then, and she went housekeeping for the smith until the day that she heard the king's son was to be married.

"If you would go to the wedding you might find service and earn something," said the blacksmith.

She went and was taken into the king's household. She heard that a pie was to be made the night before the wedding.

"May I make this pie?" she asked of the chief cook.

The chief cook grew angry and said: "You could not make this pie."

The young woman then gave him five gold coins, and the chief cook let her make the pie. She made the pie and she put the hag's castle, the stable, the tree and the lake on it, so that the king's son could see them.

When the pie was seen everyone said; "There must be a stranger in the castle."

"Send her hither," said the king.

She went up and remained with the company. During the evening all were telling tales, and at last the King of Erin said to the young woman: "Now you must tell us a tale."

"I have no tale," said she, "but I will show you a trick if you let me."

"I will, indeed," said the king.

She threw down two grains of oats, and a cock and a hen rose up from them. She threw one grain of oats between the two. The hen took the grain and the cock pecked her.

"You would not have done that to me the day you were cleaning the stable and I had to help you," said the hen.

She threw another grain; the hen took it and the cock pecked her.

"You would not have done that to me the day you were bailing out the lake and looking for the ring," said the hen.

She threw a third grain and the hen took it, and the cock pecked her.

"You would not have done that to me the day you were cutting down the great tree to get the box with the egg in it, the day the two of us fled."

All at once the king's son remembered the young woman, and knew her at that moment. He turned to his father and said:

"I'll marry no other but this woman."

The King of Erin's son then married the young woman who had been the servant girl to the hag, and they lived happily ever after.

The Apprentice Thief

A WORTHY GENTLEMAN, who lived in the south of Ireland, had a simple but very honest cottier who took care of his cattle and worked about his house, where he used to come daily.

This poor man had but one son called Billy, and this lad accustomed himself so much in following his father that he got such a haunt about this gentleman's house, he could not be kept from it a day. The gentleman, missing several articles and not knowing who to charge the theft with, but suspecting the little boy, watched him strictly till he found him twice or thrice guilty. Going to the boy's father, he told him what he had seen; "And as I know that you are an honest man," said he, "if you will make Billy bring back all that he has taken away, I will forgive him, but you must put him to some trade and not have him coming after you any longer."

The man went to his son and demanded whatever he took from the gentleman. "And if you do not return every article which you have taken away you will be hanged, and I will be turned out of my service, and I must then go and beg."

Billy was not so much afraid, but lest his father should come to be the sufferer, he gave them everything he had stolen from the gentleman; who when he had received the same was very thankful to the cottier, but told him he must put Billy away.

"Sir," says the cottier, "What trade would you allow me to apprentice him to?"

"Indeed," says the gentleman, laughing at him, "I would advise you to teach him to be a thief, for he will require little instructions."

But the cottier thought he was in earnest, being a very innocent man, and immediately went in search of a master for him. In those days Ireland abounded with woods and forests, and of course, thieves were not scarce; besides, we read of several gangs of robbers in this kingdom of old. However, this poor man and his son had not traveled far until they met with two gentlemen, as they thought, on horseback, and passing each other on the road, one of them looking back called the poor man towards him.

"Do you travel far this road?" says he.

"I do not know," says the man, "how far I may have to go, for I am looking for a master for this boy that I doubt will not be easily found."

"How is that?" says the gentleman. "Are you for teaching him so singular a trade that you imagine the country cannot afford you a master? I was in hopes that you would have hired the boy for some time, and for that reason I called you back."

"Indeed, sir," says the poor man, "I am advised by my master to teach him to be a thief, and I cannot do anything else with him."

The two horsemen laughed heartily at the fellow's simplicity, and told him he had good luck in meeting with them, for they would engage to make him perfect in that art in a very short time.

"Well," says the father, "in a good time, go with these gentlemen, and I will return home, and see that you behave yourself honestly and faithfully to your masters during the time."

They then parted, but where Billy was to remain the poor father knew nothing of, nor had he the wit to inquire anything about him. The two robbers, as we may now call them, being in search of two such lads as Billy to assist them in an enterprise that night, had no doubt from his father's discourse that he would answer the purpose well enough, and getting him up behind one of them, they rode off to a wood where they had a cave very commodiously situated for concealing stolen cattle. And putting up their horses, they went into a convenient little cabin, where they got some victuals and stopped there till night came on.

As soon as they thought the people were in bed and asleep, they mounted their horses, taking the little boy with them; they rode a considerable distance from the wood to a gentleman's dwelling, where they knew there was a great number of silver plates, with rich and valuable articles of sundry kinds, but being so strongly secured they could not get into it. They told Billy he must go into a sack and they would let him down the chimney with a rope, but that his head and hands would be free; when he came to the ground he was to loosen himself, and to gather every article he could get worth taking and put it into the sack, then tie the rope on it, and they would haul it up, and then let down the rope for him.

Afterwards Billy considered the matter a little, but seeing he could not well get over doing it, at last consented. So they put the ladder to the house, and tying the rope about him, they soon let him into the kitchen, where, loosening the rope, he soon stripped the dresser of everything valuable, with a great quantity of fine clothes and many other things he met in his way, all which he crammed into the sack. And clapping on the rope, gave the signal for the robbers to pull up, which they immediately did, and carrying it down the ladder, put it on one of the horses and immediately set off, leaving poor Billy, shut up in the gentleman's house, to shift for himself. In a short time he understood they had left him, and he did not know what to do; examining the doors he found them double locked, and the windows so high and well secured that it was impossible for him to escape. Seeing that his strength would avail nothing, he applied to stratagem, and taking a pair of tongs, went among the pots and cans, and making the greatest noise imaginable, until the servant maid awoke, and not knowing what could be in the kitchen that made such a disturbance, wakened her master, who got up, and went to the chamber door to see if he could discover what was the matter. He knew very well that no person could get into the house, and when he heard the noise in this side of the house, and the next moment in the other side, he concluded it must be a spirit of some sort; besides he conceited he saw it walking like a beast through the floor. No wonder he did, for Billy, meeting with a little bullock's hide in a corner of the house, had wrapped it round him and was rattling through pots and pans with the tongs at a terrible rate. The gentleman taking courage, and having the door half open, asked in the name of God who or what it was that was disturbing his house in such a manner.

"I am," says Billy, "one of the wandering spirits who were stationed in this house, but my time of departure being come, I found the doors all locked, of which I have no power; but rather than do you any harm, I keep this noise that you might arise and let me out, otherwise, at the hour of twelve I shall be obliged to go, and perhaps tear the roof off the house along with me."

In those days people were more easily imposed on than in this age, so that the gentleman, believing him to be a spirit, ventured up and unlocked the door, and he passed out quickly; the gentleman returned to bed well satisfied with having got rid of him so safely.

As soon as Billy found the door shut behind him he threw off
the hide, and rolling it up, put it on his shoulders and set off.
By the light of the moon he could discern the horses' tracks, and
followed on till he came to the wood, where he saw a light in
the cabin and the horses tied to a bush, as they were intending
to go on some other expedition. He went to a window which
was in the cabin, and peeping, he saw the two thieves sitting one
on each side of the fire dividing the spoil, each of them having a
large quantity of money beside him. Billy immediately took the
bullock's hide, and putting it round him like a cloak, with the
horns out from his forehead, went halfway into the window,
when one of the robbers looking up espied the large head of
horns presenting itself to him.

"Damn your eyes," says he to his comrade, "there is the devil
coming at the window; would to God we had resigned this work
before now, for I still dreaded the latter end of it."

The other in the greatest consternation ran to the door crying: "We are long enough here," and his comrade immediately
followed him; they did not venture back that night.

Billy laughed heartily at the surprise he gave the fellows, and
going into the cabin gathered all the riches he could find, both
money and goods, and putting the whole into the sack which the
robbers had made use of before, he with great difficulty got it
on one of the horses, and mounting the other, rode off for his
father's as fast as possible. Before his father was out of his bed,
Billy had the two horses put up and all the riches out of danger;
but when he returned to him so suddenly, he was greatly surprised.

"What can be the matter, Billy," says he, "that you are home
already? I doubt this is a bad way to learn a trade, to be running
away from your master every minute; this will never do."

"Indeed," says Billy, "I will stay no longer than I have learned what is necessary, and I can assure you I have as much of my trade learned as ever I will stand in need of."

In a short time, almost as soon as Billy's father, the gentleman got word that Billy was back, and sending for his father, demanded of him the reason why Billy returned so soon.

"Why, sir," says the cottier, "he tells me that he has his trade learned and can excel his masters in anything they will go about, and had no need to stay with them any longer."

"Well," says the gentleman, "I will soon know. I think it is a pretense of him to get home; but tell him, from me, that he must steal one of the horses out of the plow tomorrow, unknown to the men who will be at work, or I shall certainly have him hanged."

"That," says the cottier, "is an impossibility; you want nothing but the death of my son, and you know you may as well hang him now as wait till tomorrow for him to do the thing that none in existence can perform."

"Why," says the gentleman, "I shall give him a chance for his life; if he has learned the whole art, as he says he has, there is no fear of him, but he can do that and more; but if he has not, you may see plainly he is imposing on us both and deserves to die, for having the assurance to come back so soon after what he had already done."

The poor cottier went home weeping and lamenting the fate of his son, whom he now considered as lost.

"What is wrong with you now, Father?" says Billy. "What are you weeping for? You have heard some bad news I doubt."

"Bad enough news," says he, "for you and me both; you are to be hanged tomorrow, and what will I do without you?"

"Why," says Billy, "what have I done now that I must be hanged?"

"Because," says he, "you have come back so soon; when I

told the master that you were pretty well tried in the art, and I thought required no further instruction, he said that if you would not steal one of the horses out of the plow tomorrow, before sunset, and the plowman and driver in the field, that he would hang you; which I count an impossibility, and this is the cause of my grief, to think that this is the last night we will be together."

"How easily you are frightened, Father," says Billy. "If that is all do not trouble yourself about it, we have some time to consider on it yet, and I hope there is no danger."

However, the poor fellow still continued to lament, but Billy was not in the least concerned; at length the time came, and they began to plow, but the gentleman let them know nothing of what was done, allowing he would give Billy fair play for his life. After a little Billy went to an acquaintance he had, who had two pet rabbits, very young, and requested them for a little, and he would return them safe. His request was freely granted, and Billy set off with the rabbits to the opposite end of the field, where they were plowing, where there was a little planting of shrubbery, and concealed himself therein; at the same time letting go one of them so convenient as that they might easily see it. The plowman, happening to look that way, observed the young rabbit playing by itself among the bushes and said to his companion:

"I will hold you anything that yonder place is full of rabbits, unknown to us all, and if you go with me, you will see you will get plenty of young ones."

Away the two ran, and as they were going up to the place, Billy let go the other, and set off.

"What did I tell you?" says the plowman. "I am a rogue, but there is another. Come, you stupid fellow," says he, "don't pass a bush or place but what you search, and you will see what we will get."

During the time that the plowmen were searching the plantation Billy had got round to the other end of the field where the horses were standing, and unyoking one of them, galloped home to his father with the greatest expedition. The two plowmen searched the plantation all over, but not a rabbit was there, neither could they find those they had seen. But what was worse than all, when they came to the plow one of the horses was away, and nobody to tell what became of him.

"What the devil is this?" says one of them. "Is the horse stolen, do you think, or is somebody making sport of us?"

"I do not understand it," says the other. "We must take the horse we have and go to the house to see what is to be done."

They immediately went to their master, but when he perceived them coming home before their time he wondered what could be the matter, knowing that it was not near dinnertime. He went down to the stables.

"Boys," says he, "what is the matter?" ·

"Master," says one of them, "we have lost a horse."

"A horse," says he, "why, you blockhead, have you lost one of the horses you were plowing with and cannot tell what is become of him?"

"Indeed, sir, it is too true, for we ran after two young rabbits through the plantation, and when we came back the horse was away."

"Well," says the gentleman, "you are two smart active fellows, what will be done now?"

However, he had a guess what became of the horse, and sending for Billy's father, spoke to him as follows:

"I see that Billy has managed to steal the horse," says he, "but that does not prove that he has completely learned his trade; tell him he must take one of my horses out of the stable, and a man sitting on his back with a charged pistol in his hand,

with three other men watching at the door, without them knowing anything about it."

"I see you want to hang my son sure enough," says the father,
"for you know the art of man could not do that."

"You are mistaken," says the gentleman. "If he has the whole
trade properly learned, he can do it; besides, the watchmen shall
not be apprised in the least of the matter; I will give him every
chance for the accomplishment of it, but be assured if he fails
in the attempt he shall die."

Home the poor cottier goes once more, with tears in his eyes.

"Dear Billy," says he, "I have done with you this time. The
master will hang you if you do not steal one of his horses out of
the stable this night; and a man sitting on his back, with three
other men standing at the door well armed, to watch till morning; the night is long and we must be contriving what method is
best to be taken."

The poor father was very uneasy all day, but Billy thought
nothing about it; he sported about until evening, and then went
to an inn, where he stayed till it was dark. He then got two
bottles of the . . . tified spirits, and putting them into his pockets, placed them so that the necks could be readily perceived, and
marched off to the stable. Coming within sight of the door, he
saw a fine fire and the guards sitting round it; and creeping on
his hands and feet, he got to the back of the dunghill unper-
ceived by any of them. There happened to be a sow that was
near her littering lying on the dunghill, the sow began to be uneasy at the way Billy was tormenting her; so that the watch concluded that she was sick (some of them knowing that she was at
her time or near it), and taking a lanthorn with them, went to
the back of the dunghill, where they found Billy all covered with
dung, and in so drunken a condition that they really imagined he
was lost.

"We must," says one of them, "bring the creature to the fire, for he will not survive otherwise, and we ought to help the distressed when we meet with them."

Then, taking Billy in their arms, they lifted him up and carried him tenderly to the fire, where they made him a bed of clean straw and put him carefully on it. All this time Billy appeared senseless and impotent, seemingly in such a condition as rendered it difficult to determine whether he was dead or alive. Seeing the bottles in his pocket, one of them drew them out and found them both full.

"Come all here," says he, "and I will treat you; the night is cold and here is something to warm us; this poor fellow had got too much already and we deserve something for saving the poor divel's life."

Saying these words, he applied the bottle to his mouth and took a hearty draught. He then handed it to his comrade, and so from one to another till it came to the one on horseback in the stable, and going in gave him what remained. After some little time the spirits began to enliven them, and they resolved to empty the other bottle, and in a short time finished it also. In some little time their speech began to fail, and Billy saw with pleasure one falling here, another there, till in short they were all fallen asleep around him, and he that was on horseback snoring in the middle of the stable. Billy, seeing them in this posture, arose and stripped them of their clothes and arms, and mounting his horse, rode off to his father's house and told him how he had succeeded, at which he was exceedingly surprised. The next morning the gentleman sent for the old man, and said that although his son had shown himself tolerably dexterous, yet he must try him once more. The gentleman informed him that Billy must take the sheet from under himself and his wife when in bed.

"I will sit up all night with a charged musket, and two or three candles burning in the room; should he succeed in this he will be master of his trade, and I shall trouble him no more."

In vain did the poor old man plead the impossibility of the task. The gentleman was peremptory in his demand. He went home and with tears in his eyes told Billy the whole affair, saying he did not ever expect to see him alive as it was out of his power to accomplish the undertaking.

"Dear Father," said the boy, "do not grieve yourself for me, I have no doubt but I will overcome this difficulty."

At night, Billy went to the graveyard, and lifting the body of a man who had been buried that day, dressed him in his own clothes and carried him on his back to the gentleman's house, and tying a rope round the body of the corpse, dropped it down the chimney. As soon as the body appeared, the gentleman exclaimed:

"Here comes Billy, but I will put the rogue out of the world."

So saying, he fired, and Billy letting go, he supposed he had actually killed him. The lady, terrified at the supposed crime her husband had committed, and dreading a discovery, put out the candles and desired her husband to take the body away and bury it somewhere. No sooner did he come out with the body than Billy slipped in, and soon found his way to the lady's bedchamber. She asked him if he had buried the body.

"Indeed, I could not, it was so cold; but as soon as I warm myself in bed I will complete the job."

Having got into bed, he soon found means to accomplish the enterprise. On pretense of finishing the interment of the corpse, he slipped out of bed, taking the sheet along with him, and ran home to his father.

Billy had scarcely left the house when the gentleman returned.

"No person will discover where the body is, he is so well covered," said he to the lady.

"You have not been long this time," said she.

"I have not been more than once."

"You told me," returned she, "a few minutes ago that until you warmed yourself in bed, you could not complete the interment of the body."

"I am afraid," said he, "Billy has outwitted us both," and lighting a candle, found to his great mortification that the sheet had actually been taken away. The disgrace of this affair was so great that he could not stop in the place, but sold all his lands and property, and went to America.

The Blacksmith

*O*NCE UPON a time, when pigs were swine, and swallows built their nests in old men's beards, there lived in the north of Ireland, in a place called the Low Glens, one Robin, a blacksmith, who had been brought up to the particular branch of making plow-irons: in those days Ireland was particularly infested with a kind of small beings called fairies, who inhabited those hills and mounts so common in the north of Ireland.

One day as he was leaning over the shop door, not being very busy, he observed a little boy in green, mounted on a horse, who rode up to the door and asked Robin to shoe the horse for him.

"I would and welcome," says Robin, "if I could, but the divel a thing I can make but plow-irons."

"Well," said the boy, "if you would give me leave I would shoe him myself."

"And welcome," said Robin.

The boy seized a hatchet, and going out, cut the feet off his horse, brought them in, and put them on the hearth. He then blew up the fire about them, and immediately pulled out the feet with a new set of shoes on them, went out and put them on his horse, and returning Robin thanks, rode off.

"Bless me," cried Robin, "if that be the way to shoe horses I surely can do it; my coal horse wants shoes and I'll shoe him as I have nothing to do at present."

Robin goes out, cuts the feet off his horse, brings them in to the hearth, and blows up the fire about them; but in a short time, instead of pulling them out shod, as the boy did, he burnt them to pieces.

"Why," said Robin to himself, "I thought I had learnt how to do this, but I have missed it; and what can I make of it now?"

In a few days afterwards, as Robin was musing over the shop door, he sees the same little green-coated boy riding into the shop with an old woman before and another behind him. Coming up to Robin, he demanded of him to make him a new and young woman out of the two old ones.

"Dear help you," said Robin, "I never could make anything but plow-irons."

"Well," said the boy, "perhaps you would oblige me with the use of the shop and I will do it myself."

"You are very welcome," says Robin, "to anything I have."

The boy thanked him and brought in the old women and clapped them both in the fire; at last, to Robin's great surprise, he pulled out a beautiful young woman in place of the two old ones, mounted his horse, and Robin helped up the young woman behind him, when he departed in great friendship.

When the boy was gone, Robin thought he could do it as well as him, "And," said he, "I have my mother and mother-in-law in the corner disputing and quarreling every day, and I think it is better to have one good young woman than to have two fools." Accordingly, Robin went into the house and brought out the two old women to the shop, crushed them into the fire and blew hard at the bellows; but in a short time he deprived them of life and reduced them to cinders. Robin became so alarmed at the horrible state he had reduced his household to that he rushed out of the door and continued running on during the whole day, without so much as looking behind him, or knowing where he

THE BLACKSMITH

went. At last, being very much fatigued, he was inclined to stop
about the middle of a high mountain he was crossing, but hearing the sound of a whistle he redoubled his pace till he arrived at
the top, where he sat down breathless. Immediately up comes a
little boy with a green jacket, but barefooted, who asked Robin
if he was in need of a boy.

Robin, recovering himself a little and finding he was not pursued, told him he had no need of a boy, not knowing how to
bring himself through the world.

"No matter," said the boy, "if you do not stand in need of me
at present, I might be of service to you if you have to travel"; on
which Robin agreed to take the boy along with him.

After traveling for some time, and conversing on different
subjects, "What trade do you follow?" said the boy.

"Why," says Robin, "I can do a little at the smith trade."

"That answers very well," said he, "for there is a great lord
in Dublin that has made a bet of a thousand pounds that there
is not a smith in all Ireland can do what his smith can do, and I
think it would be a good way for you to try and win it."

"Indeed," said Robin, "I would have no chance, for all ever I
could do was making plow-irons."

"Well, I will tell you what you will do," said the boy. "Come
along with me to Dublin, and say that you are come to win the
bet, and that you will outdo his lordship's smith; and when
you are brought forward for trial, they will be wishing you to
show something first, but you must decline it, and tell his lordship that his smith shall have the honor of beginning the work,
and whatever he does, don't you be surprised, but make light of
it; then command me, and don't be afraid, for I will certainly
win you a thousand pounds."

By the encouragement Robin got from the boy, and the expectation of getting such a sum of money, he consented to go to Dublin, and accordingly they set off and in a short time arrived in the city, where Robin waited on his lordship and told him that he would undertake to match his smith, let the business be what it would. A day was then appointed for the trial, his lordship and a great number of spectators were present, who were surprised at the mean appearance of Robin and his boy.

However, Robin was asked to do something, who wisely shifted it, saying he would be very sorry not to give the honor of the first trick to his lordship's smith; at which he was called forth to the bellows. When the fire was well kindled, to the great surprise of all present, he blew a great shower of wheat out of the fire which fell through all the shop. Then they demanded of Robin to try what he could do.

"Pho!" said Robin, as if he thought nothing of what was done. "Come," said he to the boy, "I think I showed you something like that."

The boy goes then to the bellows and blew out a great flock of pigeons, who soon devoured all the grain and then disappeared.

The Dublin smith, sorely vexed that such a boy as him should outdo him, goes a second time to the bellows, and blew a fine trout out of the hearth, who jumped into a little river that was running by the shop door and was seen no more at that time.

Robin then said to the boy: "Come, you must bring us yon trout back again, to let the gentlemen see we can do something."

Away the boy goes, and blew a large otter out of the hearth, who immediately leaped into the river and in a short time returned with it in his mouth, and then disappeared. All present allowed that it was a folly to attempt a competition any further.

Accordingly, the gentleman gave Robin the money, and he

and his boy set off from Dublin, pleased with what he had made. As they were walking along the road, the boy said to his master:

"I will tell you what we will do now. The King of Scotland is lying very bad at present, and is given up by all his physicians; for which he has proclaimed a sack of gold and a horse to carry it to anyone that will cure him of his disorder; now you must go pass for the doctor and cure the king."

"Bless me," said Robin, "how could I cure him, that can do nothing but make plow-irons?"

"No matter for that," said the boy, "you must personate the doctor and I will perform the cure, and I will help you before I leave you, although you thought you would have no need of me when you first met with me."

Robin at last consented, and they set off for Scotland, where in a short time they arrived at the palace.

"Now," said the boy to Robin, "when you see the king, order every soul in the chamber to retire and cause the maid to bring you a pot of water, and I will do the rest."

Accordingly, it was made known at the court that there was a great doctor from Ireland who would cure the king in a short time. Robin was readily admitted, and when he had done all that the boy had told him, he then shut the chamber door, and his boy then went to the bedside of the king, and as Robin thought, cut the head off him and put it into the pot of water on the fire. He then took out of his pocket a short spoon with which he stirred the head about for some time. At length, when it boiled a good while, he took it out of the pot and put it on the king again, on which he arose whole and sound.

There was great rejoicing for the king's recovery, and Robin received his promised reward. He now began to think himself rich enough to return home. Accordingly, he and his boy set off for Ireland, and as they were traveling along the road the boy began to complain of his feet, and demanded a pair of shoes from him, saying it would be all he would ask for his service. Robin, being of a miserly disposition, and thinking himself solely in possession of all the riches, could not think of parting with any of it, and turned about to strike the boy. But the boy, the horse, and all the gold were gone, leaving his master not one penny, as the thousand pounds he won in Dublin was tied in the mouth of the sack.

Robin, at this unexpected accident, was greatly alarmed, having nothing to support him. Traveling on, he came to a post town, where he heard that the King of England was very ill of the same complaint that the King of Scotland had, and that there was the same reward offered for curing him. Robin began to think he could certainly cure the king, knowing perfectly, as he thought, the means the boy had used with the King of Scotland.

Accordingly, he agreed with the master of a ship, who in a short time landed him in London, where he soon made known he was the same person who performed such wonders in Scotland, and was come to relieve His Majesty in like manner. Immediately he got admittance, and as the boy had done before, he ordered the maid to bring him a pot and some water, and then all to retire.

When Robin was left alone, he locked the chamber door, and putting on the pot full of water, he cut off the head of the king and put it in the pot, where it began to boil. But to Robin's great surprise it soon boiled asunder in the pot, and he could not get it together again. Not knowing what to do, he heard a rap at the chamber door, and thinking it was one of the household, cries:

"You cannot get in yet."

"Why, will you not let your barefooted boy in?" says he at the door. "I am sure I will do you no harm!"

"Oh, my dear fellow," said Robin, "but I am glad to see you," running to the door and letting him in.

"What are you doing here, master?" said the boy.

"Ah, my dear," says Robin, "I thought to cure the king as you had done, but I cannot manage it, and I do not know what to do."

The boy then goes to the bed, looks at the king, and taking out his cutty spoon, stirred the head about in the pot, and then took it out, brought it to the king, fitted it exactly on him, and in a minute had him sound and whole as ever.

The greatest rejoicings for the recovery of the king that could be were throughout the palace, and Robin and his boy were feasted for a week. Robin then received the reward, and rejoicing at his good fortune, they set off for Ireland.

Before they had gone very far the boy began to complain of the soreness of his feet, and asked Robin if he would give him the price of a pair of shoes, for he could not travel barefooted any farther.

"Indeed," said Robin, "you may take what you please, there is the whole sack to you, it was yourself won it, and you are welcome to it."

"Well," said the boy, "had you been so generous at first, I would not have deserted you when I did, but I wanted to open your eyes and to teach you not to be too covetous. And now, Robin," said he, "I am going to leave you, and you will never see me more; my design when I first appeared to you was to make your fortune; it was I who came to your shop and caused you to kill your mother and mother-in-law, and your coal horse; but you will get them all living yet. I preserved them as I did the king when you cut the head off him. Now I think you have plenty, take this load of gold home, and I will meet you there with what I took from you."

With that the boy disappeared, and Robin drove on as fast as he could. After instructing Robin how to lay out his money to the best advantage, he disappeared, and never was seen afterwards.

Peter Megrab and His Brother John

*T*HERE LIVED a woman who was married to a man of the name of Megrab, and having one child, Peter, the husband died. She was again married to one Craig and bore him a son; he died, and left her a widow a second time. However, she took great care of her two sons, Peter Megrab and John Craig. The former was a stout, hardy fellow, but John was a very weak child. No brother could love another better than Peter did John, insomuch that he could scarce let him out of his sight.

They both grew up to men's estate, and it at last happened that Peter was under the necessity of leaving his wife and family to seek employment in another part of the country. After traveling all day he came to a large house, and when he asked the porter if he would give him lodging for the night, he kindly made him welcome.

"But," said he, "if my master were at home he would give you a castle to lodge in, and a good sum of money for it."

"What," said Peter, "is it haunted with evil spirits, or what is the matter that one should be paid for staying in it?"

"I do not know the reason, but there is nobody willing to come near, although this gentleman offers a quart of gold to anyone who will stay one night in it."

"By Jove," said Peter, "if he gives me a quart of gold I will stay in it if the devil were in it."

"Well," said the porter, "he will soon return and I will tell him."

Accordingly, the gentleman returned, and the porter told him that there was a hardy-looking fellow in the house that would lodge in the castle for the sum proposed.

"Call him out," said he, "until I speak to him."

Peter was called, and the gentleman asked him if he would take charge of his castle that night for a quart of gold.

"I will," said Peter, "but I must have a good fire and candles."

"You shall have that," said the gentleman, "and you may go to it as soon as you please."

Peter then went to the castle, where there was plenty of firing and candles left him.

When he had got a good fire on, and everything fixed, he took a candle in one hand and his sword in the other, and went through many rooms richly furnished; and what most surprised him was that everything belonging to the castle was in its own place, and yet no appearance of any inhabitant having been there for a long time before.

When he had tired himself going through the castle he sat down at the fire, took out his pipe and began to smoke. He had not sat long until he heard the noise of feet upstairs, and presently he saw two gentlemen coming towards the fire, and as he thought sat down. One of them was older and richer-dressed than the other.

Peter was not in the least concerned, till at length they came on each side of him, and soon crushed him off his seat and pressed him to the floor. Taking courage, he said: "In the name of God, gentlemen, what do you want, or why do you trouble me?"

"Ah!" said the old-looking gentleman. "You are a happy man, for you have done good to yourself and us: sit down and hearken to what I will tell you."

Peter got up on his seat, and the old man began as follows:

"Know, my brave fellow, that I was lord of this castle, and that is my son who has employed you to stay here this night; tell him in the morning that when he was on his mother's knee one night, when she and most of the family were absent, I and my body servant, whom you see along with me, were murdered by John Curry for the sake of the great riches which the castle contains. No one ever knew what became of us, and my wife through grief died in a short time after, and left my son sole heir of all my estates and property; but from the night we were murdered until this moment, no one could dwell in this castle, which obliged my son to build the house you now see him in. Tell him we are both buried in my own cellar, and that he must get our corpses raised and interred in the churchyard, and that is the same John Curry, that is living in the next town at present, who is guilty; get him immediately apprehended, and if your evidence is not sufficient to convict him, I shall myself appear in court a witness against him. Tell my son also that I unjustly deprived a poor widow of a small farm of land, and that he must return the same immediately.

"Now, my brave fellow, come along with me, and I will show you all the riches in the castle, and in return I will give you something superior to all the gold in the world."

Then taking a candle, he led him through a variety of rooms, until they came to a cellar where he showed him an immense quantity of gold. After this he led Peter into a small apartment where there was a desk, and taking out a small piece of cloth, "Here," said he, "when you want meat, you have no more to do than to spread this cloth, and wish for any sort of victuals you please, and they will immediately appear before you."

The cock crowing, the old man instantly vanished, and Peter returned to his chamber, where he remained until morning, when he informed the gentleman all that had happened. John Curry was immediately apprehended, and shortly after brought to trial. When Peter attended to give evidence, "What," says the judge, "is there no other proof to be produced than what this impostor thinks proper to swear to?" Instantly a most dreadful rumbling noise was heard in the court: "Here am I that was murdered by the prisoner at the bar."

No more evidence was necessary, and sentence of death was accordingly pronounced against him. Peter was paid according to his contract, and having taken farewell of his master, pursued his journey.

Having everything that a man could wish for, viz., plenty of money, and the best victuals he thought proper to call for, he determined to return home by the desert; after traveling for three days without meeting a single creature, he at last saw a man on horseback advancing towards him. On coming up he saluted him, and asked if he had traveled far that way.

"I have," said the man, "traveled these three days, and you are the first man I have met, and I have tasted but one meal during that time."

"Well," said Peter, "stop a little, and I will have something will help you." So taking out his cloth, he spread it on the ground and instantly they had plenty before them.

"Bless me," said the stranger, "you need not care where you travel; I thought I had the greatest curiosity in the world, but yours surpasses it."

"What have you?" said Peter.

"I have a box," said he, "and when you open it, you have an invisible army at your command, both horse and foot, all invisible."

Peter, being of a ready wit, thought if he had the box along with his cloth he would do well; so asking to look at the box, and finding the words of the stranger true, he offered to exchange, to which the stranger readily consented, thinking the cloth of far more use to him than the box. Peter put the box into his pocket, and the other the cloth in his, and after returning Peter sincere thanks for his kind treat, they departed, each going his own road. Peter had not gone far until he opened his box, and his army appearing, as usual, he ordered them to bring back the cloth. In a moment they returned with the cloth, at which he was very glad, and closing them up in his box again, proceeded on his journey. He now considered that he was fully fitted for life, and resolved to push home as fast as possible.

Having at last arrived in his own country, he was surprised to see what a fine castle his brother John had, and his little cabin in its former state. By the time he got home, his shoes and stockings were not worth one penny. In this wretched state he entered the house, where his wife and children were glad to see him once more; but when his wife saw the state he was in, and no appearance of any fortune he had made, her joy was soon turned into ridicule.

"What have you been doing all this time," said she, "that you have not a penny home with you? Your brother was but a short time away, and see what a fortune he has made; built a fine castle, purchased land, and lives like a gentleman."

"Well, dear," said Peter, "every man's fortune is not alike; did my brother give you nothing to help you, when he came home with so much riches?"

"Indeed, he was no such fool as to give me any of it. I believe we are to be in poverty all our days; I had some hopes you had made something, but now I see it is over."

"I cannot help it," said Peter, "but I have some money with which I intend to treat my neighbors, who were sorry at my going away."

"You are surely jesting, Peter," said she; "my children and I would have more need of the money than to lay it out in such a foolish manner."

Early next morning, Peter got up and invited all his neighbors to dine with him that day at one o'clock. When John Craig heard that his brother was returned, he called on him, but finding him poor and naked, appeared indifferent about him.

Peter, observing with what disdain his brother looked upon him, turned and asked him the reason why he did not give part of his gold to his wife when he came home.

"Indeed," said he, "I bought it dear; I almost lost my life before I got it home."

"I see," said Peter, "for that reason you would keep all; well, we must do without it."

Dinnertime was now drawing nigh, and no sign of anything. At length the people began to come, and Peter's wife became quite impatient.

"I believe," said she, "that it was to affront yourself and me forever you did this, to invite the whole village to dine with you, and not one morsel to give them, nor, I believe, one penny to get anything with."

"Take time, woman," said Peter, "it is not dinnertime yet."

At last Peter went out, placed them in a circle on the green, and standing in the midst, took out his cloth and spread it on the ground, and no sooner wished, as usual, than it was covered with the choicest meat and drink in abundance, to the astonishment of all present.

The fame of Peter's tablecloth came to the king's ears, and he immediately sent a messenger to Peter, demanding the wonderful tablecloth.

"Well," said Peter, "it is a poor thing a man cannot enjoy the fruit of his own labor; you may tell His Majesty that I dearly bought the cloth, and that I will not part with it for any man."

The king, greatly enraged at so positive a refusal, immediately sent a strong guard to bring him before him. Peter, knowing what would be the result of his denial, put himself on his guard, and espying the guard coming towards him, he took out his box, and his invincible army asked him what they had to do.

"Go, slay every man in the guard but one, that he may bring the tidings to the king."

No sooner was command given than Peter saw the guard falling dead on the ground, but one, as he had ordered, who had galloped off in a great fear and surprise, not knowing what to think of their defeat. He told the king that before they came to Peter's house they were all but himself cut off by some invisible power. The king, more enraged than ever, went forth at the head of his chief guards, and drew near to Peter's house, which when Peter observed, he took his box and commanded his army to kill all except the king. The king now saw his army cut off and lying dead on the field, and could not think how, or by what means. By this time Peter had enclosed his army in his box, and ventured up to the king, who vowed vengeance on Peter and all belonging to him throughout the kingdom.

"Well," said Peter, "Your Majesty had no right to say so, for I am a good subject and never wished Your Majesty any harm; consider that it was in my power to destroy Your Majesty's person as well as the guards; besides, sire, I can be of more service to my king and country than a number of your subjects, and when occasion requires, I am ready to undertake any service towards the support of Your Majesty's person and property."

The candid manner in which Peter told his story so wrought upon the king that he took him to the palace along with him, and soon after he became one of His Majesty's principal ministers of state.

The Adventures of the Farmer
and the Red Wizard

LONG BEFORE the Danes ever thought of coming to Ireland, or
of making beer out of the flowers of the heather, there lived in
Ballydehob in the south of Ireland a farmer who was middling
rich, for he was an industrious, thrifty man who had a fair
share of the world's goods. He had only one son and there was
no doubt but that he loved him dearly. It is seldom, however,
that a frugal father has a thrifty son, and that was the case with
the farmer. After a long life of hard work the old man died,
as happens, and will happen to everyone of the race of men,
and as soon as he did the young man got his father's money
into his own hands. There was a great lot of it there, both gold
and silver, and it was little the proud foolish fellow thought
that he would ever come to the end of it. To increase, or to
make safe, his nest egg was the last thought in his head, so he
began to spend his money like water.

He went on spending like this for a few years until, at last, he
saw that he was coming to the end of his money. Then when he
hadn't a penny left he began to search every hole and corner
in the house where he thought his father might have hidden
some silver or gold, and he was lucky enough to find a purse
full of sovereigns stuck up in the thatch. But it did not do him

much good, for instead of giving up his foolish ways and turning over a new leaf, he started to drink and gamble as before, and he never stopped until he had lost all his father had left him, and with it his good name and his self-respect. He had to mortgage his land, and in spite of that he was not able to pay his debts. Even with all his misfortune he had as little sense as ever. He followed the hunt, and he kept up every other foolishness and extravagance that he had gone in for since his father's death.

One day when he was coming home tired and weary, on the road near his own house he met an old man who seemed to be a half fool. He was sitting at his ease behind a high furze hedge. They began to talk to one another. The man told him that he was called the Red Wizard, and that it was his hard fate, ever since he was born, to be given to a great love of dicing, even though all he gained by it, too often, was hardship and trouble. He asked the farmer then would he play a game with him. The farmer said he would but that he had not a lot of money to bet.

The Red Wizard then said to him:

> "Give up your brawling and prattling,
>   Drinking at feast and at fair;
> The man who sets shillings a-rattling
> On counters for whiskey and beer
> Will soon see the day
> When his money galore
> Is money no more
> And along the highway
> With his feet in the dust
> He must beg for his crust
> At door after door."

THE ADVENTURES OF THE FARMER AND THE RED WIZARD

"That's good advice," said the farmer, "if I could only follow it."

The wizard was a clever, scornful person who knew how to play clever tricks with magic. Any chance he got to do mischief he never missed it, but the farmer believed him to be an honest poor fellow.

The wizard now took a die out of his pocket and they began to play. They made a bargain that the wizard would put a hundred pounds against every crown that the farmer would bet, and the farmer was very satisfied. In a short time he had won a good sum and the wizard paid him, as he had promised. The farmer went home in high spirits and in great heart. From that on he became more sensible, and he began to carry out every bargain he made and to attend to his work.

Time went by until one day the farmer met the Red Wizard again. They talked together for a little while, and then the Red Wizard asked him to play a game with him once more.

"What will you claim from me this time, if you beat me?" asked the farmer. "For it is right that we should make our bargain before we begin."

"It isn't for money we will play this time," said the wizard, "but we will postpone our conditions until we see which of us is the better man."

"Very well," said the farmer, "that suits me."

They began to play then, very carefully and earnestly, until in the end the farmer won.

"That was a stroke of bad luck for me," said the wizard, "and I think you did not play fair, but let it be. I assure you I'll repay you the compliment some day. Tell me now," said he, "what forfeit do you ask me to pay?"

"I put you under heavy bonds," said the farmer, "to have

the most beautiful woman in the world for me, at my house, two weeks from tomorrow, so that I may marry her."

"That's a hard task," said the wizard, "and it puts me into a great dilemma, but I think I will be able to satisfy you."

The farmer was very pleased to hear this, and he passed the time happily until the day fixed with the wizard. At sunrise on that day his servant girl came to the door of his room and said that there was a young woman, resembling a king's daughter in her appearance and in her bearing, waiting in the hall, and that she never saw her like for beauty.

The farmer hurried to meet her. The noble lady seemed afraid of him at first, but the farmer spoke to her in a gentle and friendly tone and she seemed to lose her dread. They got married then and they were very happy and free from care for twenty years, and about that time the farmer got a wish to have another game with the wizard.

"It is my opinion," said his wife, "that you will meet with misfortune if you have anything more to do with that wizard."

But it was no use for her to be trying to advise him. He started off one fine evening and he kept on walking till he came to the place in the glen where it was usual for the wizard to sit, and he hoped to see him there. He was not mistaken, for there he was, under the hedge of furze where he used to be. The wizard gave the farmer a very friendly welcome, and he asked him how he had been faring since last they had met. The farmer told him word by word how he had been, and as they were talking the wizard suddenly said that he had a terrible desire to play another game with the farmer, and that he could not help his evil inclination.

"Let us play one game," said he, "and we will play for the same terms as the last time."

The farmer did not need much pressing, and they began to play for the third time, but before they started they made the bargain that whoever won could put any penalty he wished on his partner. The proverb says that it isn't every day that fair-haired Donal gets married, and you could say the same about the farmer and his friendship with the Red Wizard. As clever as the farmer thought he was, the Red Wizard was much more clever. After spending a little while playing this time, the Red Wizard won. The farmer shook with fear and fell down in a faint. After a quarter of an hour the farmer came to himself, but a terrible fit of shaking seized him at the thought of the penalty the Red Wizard would put on him for losing the game.

"Stand up now, until I will tell you what forfeit I am going to make you pay," said the Red Wizard.

"Tell me quickly what you are going to ask of me," said the farmer, as he stood up, "for I suppose I have no chance of getting out of it."

"I put you under bonds," said the Red Wizard, "to find out for me who stole the Golden Boat, who killed the Giant O'Dowd, and to get for me the Sword of Light from the Youthful Warrior in the Eastern World, and have it here for me a year and a day from today. Goodbye to you now, and 'tis many a straight and crooked road you will travel in that time."

It was with a heart heavy with sorrow that the farmer went home. After a while his wife noticed that there was some trouble preying on his mind, and she had a strong suspicion that it was the deceitful trickery of the wizard that was causing the trouble. She asked him how he had spent his time since he had left the house, and what had happened to put him into such a state of grief. The farmer knew that his wife was very clever, as clever as the wizard, and that it would be no good to keep the truth from her, so he told her how he had lost to the Red Wizard, and of the terrible forfeit he had put on him. "And that," said he, "is the cause of all my torment."

"If you had taken my advice about keeping away from the wizard," said she, "you wouldn't have that story to tell now. He has you caught securely in a dangerous trap now, but I will tell you what to do, and maybe you will succeed in finding out the answers to his questions, and in getting him the Sword of Light from the Youthful Warrior in the Eastern World. But you must have courage and do as I tell you, and I warn you 'tis many a warrior has lost his life in trying to perform these three tasks."

Then she told him what he would have to do, and after that she put him to sleep with fairy music.

On the following morning, at the break of day, the farmer's wife got up and made food ready for her husband to take with him. When the food was ready she went out into the fields and took a long thread out of her pocket and she let it float on the wind and she called out loudly once or twice. It wasn't long till a slender brown steed came towards her and he was already saddled and bridled. She brought him into the stable yard to her husband then and said:

"It is time for you to be going now, and may my blessing go with you."

The farmer kissed his wife, got up on the horse, and as he took to the road a shower of tears fell from his eyes. The steed went with the speed of the wind, and the farmer could not tell whether they were going east or west, for they were going so quickly he could hardly see anything. Then they came to the edge of the sea, but that did not stop the steed, for she flew over the waves of the sea as lightly as an eagle would clear the top of a hill. It wasn't long till the farmer was well out of sight of quay or harbor.

He went on traveling then till the sun went down and then darkness began to fall around them. It was about this time that they came on to land again, and then the steed went quicker than ever, and never slackened his pace till he drew up on a smooth, green lawn in front of a castle, high and broad and freshly lime-washed. The steed started to neigh. The farmer knew that she must be giving a warning to the people of the castle, for the door opened at once and a number of servants came out, took his horse and escorted himself into the hall.

It was the king of the country who was living in the castle, and both he and his wife greeted the farmer with a hundred thousand welcomes. They told him that they were the father and mother of his wife and they asked him for news of their daughter and how she liked living in Erin. Then they had food and drink set before him, and he told them why he was going to the Eastern World, and he asked them for guidance.

"Well now," said the king, "the Red Wizard, the Youthful Warrior and myself are three brothers. And though the Red Wizard is the youngest of us, he is cunning and mean and he has always worked against us. He coveted the Sword of Light that the Youthful Warrior owns, and he asked my help to steal it, but I had no wish to do any wrong to my brother, since that fine, warmhearted man never did any harm to anyone, and 'tis many a noble and courageous thing he did throughout his life. So he avenged himself on me by stealing my daughter and taking her away to Erin, and to avenge himself on the Youthful Warrior he played dice with you to trap you, and to send you for the Sword of Light and for the answers to the hidden questions.

"The Youthful Warrior is living in Strong Fort, two miles from here. That fort has high walls all around it, and inside the walls there are fierce dragons always on watch, and if they catch you they would eat you alive. If you could escape the first day and the second day, you need not fear them from that on. It is a place of safety for the Youthful Warrior and no one is allowed to go near the house who is not known to the dragons. If you ride the brindled horse that I will give you, he will take you over the gate. Don't mind who will see you but shout out in a loud voice that you want the Sword of Light, and that you want to know who stole the Golden Boat and who killed the Giant O'Dowd. Don't make the shortest delay after that, but turn your horse around and make off with all the speed you can, and come back here."

On the following morning the farmer mounted the brindled horse that his wife's father had given him, and he rode off full of courage till he came to the high walls that were all around the Strong Fort. Then the brindled horse tossed his head, rose in the air like a bird, made a sprightly leap over the walls, and before anyone could know he was there the farmer called out in a loud voice to have the Sword of Light brought out to him, and to tell him who stole the Golden Boat and who killed the Giant O'Dowd. At that the dragons uttered such a scream of hate that the high walls shook around him as they were making for him with their mouths open to swallow him. Like a flash of lightning he turned his horse around and faced him to the wall. With one leap the horse cleared the wall but he broke his two hind legs in coming down. The farmer made off on foot then, and it was near nightfall when he reached the castle of his wife's father, but he was without a scratch or a wound of any kind, and everyone was delighted to see him come back safe.

He went back to the Strong Fort the next day on another horse that he got from his wife's father. He leaped over the wall and shouted out his two questions and asked for the Sword of

Light, but he had scarcely finished when the dragons were nearly upon him, their red gullets open as they roared with rage. He only just managed to escape from their jaws as his horse rose up over the wall in a flying leap. Everyone in the court had a hundred thousand welcomes before him on that night too.

"All the dragons will be asleep today," said the king to the farmer on the morning of the third day. "They're worn-out with weariness from having to keep watch without stop for the last two days. I'd say they will never notice you going in today. Go straight in the door of the Strong Fort and you'll get everything you want inside."

The farmer rode off on his horse then and he followed the advice of his wife's father. He went in the door and no one tried to stop him. The dragons were all sound asleep, and though by accident he trod on the foot of one of them, he never stirred but kept on snoring away for himself.

He went through the fine, wide hall and it seemed to the farmer that it was the most beautiful, well-made castle anyone ever saw. At the end of the hall he saw a broad staircase in front of him and he went up. On the first floor he heard some people talking in one of the rooms. He knocked on the door and asked if he might go in.

"Come in and welcome," said a man who opened the door. "Since you were able to destroy all the firm fortifications that were protecting us and that we thought would withstand any raid, we may as well tell you to come in. Sit down now and tell us of what people you are and what put it into your head to come here and invade us."

"I have come here from a great distance," said the farmer.

"'Tis a pity you came," said the nobleman. "But since you have shown such courage and skill I will not reproach you. It is many a brave warrior who came to his end trying to get into this fortress."

"Well now," said the farmer, "since I'm in I may as well tell you what I want and what brought me here. I only want the Sword of Light and to get information as to who stole the Golden Boat and who killed the Giant O'Dowd."

"I think that you already know that I am the Youthful Warrior," said the nobleman. "And there yonder, hanging on the wall, is the Sword of Light; you can take it as a present from me now. It gives out so much light that you can see anything near it in the darkness of night as well and as clearly as in the broad noonday. I will tell you now how I got the Golden Boat and how I killed the Giant O'Dowd by the strength of my arm. There is no one here listening to me but my wife, and she can contradict me if she thinks that I am not telling the truth.

"When I was a fine handsome youth I took a notion to see foreign people and distant countries, and to find out how they lived in these distant places. So I got into a boat and sailed along by the shores of the world's regions and where did I come to but Greece. I got acquainted with the King of Greece, who had a daughter whose like for beauty could not be found. I was not long there till I fell in love with her and we got married, with the good wishes of her mother and father. But as there isn't a place under the heavens where I want to live but in my native land, I begged her to come home with me. She refused my request and she said that she did not care a straw for me. I paid little heed to what she was saying, for I knew that she was young and silly. Her parents advised her to go with me, and in order to coax her to do so her father gave her a present of a magic wand that he had owned for many years, but she would not come with me till I lived with her in the Eastern World first. And so I did, but she tormented the heart inside in me with her vanity and her tantrums, and one day when I refused to give her her own way she struck me with the magic wand and turned me into a horse. All the same I did not lose my human mind and senses. Now and again I would give a kick to anyone who would try to ride me, and I would throw them under my hooves. At other times I would rend and tear with my teeth anyone who would come near me. So news of my bad temper went around and everyone was afraid of me and I had a fine idle life. This did not please my wife, for she was spiteful and wished to see me worked hard. She came on me one day as I was sunning myself with great content under a tree. 'You have no right to be at your ease there,' she said, and she stuck a spike into my back. Anger seized me, for she had been constantly tormenting me, and I could not let that insult go with her. So I kicked her in the forehead and she fell down on the ground and there was not as much as a breath of life left in her body. A servant found her unconscious and brought her home, and after a great deal of care she got better and her strength came back to her. But that was not joyful news for me, for I believed that she never stopped, day or night, plotting the best way to destroy me.

"One fine day, as ill luck would have it, she met me when I was alone and she struck me with her magic wand again and turned me into a wolf. She set the dogs after me and 'twas only by my great speed that I got away from them at all, but in the end they caught up with me, and they were going to tear me to pieces when the King of Greece came along. He did not know who I was, since my wife had told him long before that I had gone off to the Western World and that she did not know whether I was dead or alive.

"I bowed to him as well as I was able. He saw the trace of tears on my cheek and he took pity on me. He thought there

was something peculiar in my movements. I followed him home
and every day that went by our love for each other increased. My
wife was angry at seeing this, and since it was not in her power
to kill me she did her best to get her father to agree to send
me away, but it was no use for her because he paid little heed
to what she said.

"It was usual for me to be in the room where our child used
to be asleep in his cradle, for I was very tame. One day she
slipped in and she sprinkled blood on me, and rubbed some
more of it on the sleeping child, so that people would think I
had tried to kill it. Then she began shouting and roaring until
her father and everyone in the house heard her. They all ran to
her to find out what was the cause of her trouble. She com-
plained of me bitterly and said that I had attacked the child, and
only that she managed to take it away from me I would have
killed it. They all turned on me then and they nearly killed me,
but my wife's father, the King of Greece, said it would be better
to turn me loose and to give me a chance to live in my own
way in the forest.

"Great hardships and misfortunes came on me from the time I
was driven off. I suffered much from hunger and thirst and I
had not a place to lie down. One day I made up my mind that
I would head for the sea, where I might find a fish or a carcass
thrown up by the waves that would take the hunger from me.
I was walking along the high cliffs, where the waves were breaking against the rocks below and making a noise like thunder,
when I saw the finest ship that anyone's eye ever fell on. It
came in close to where I was and it was tossing up and down
on the water. I swam out towards it, as I thought there might
be some bread or meat floating around it. When I drew close to it
I could see that someone on board had a fishing rod out over the
side. I went to the stern where the fishing rod was and I swam

underneath it, and no sooner did I pass under it than my own shape and my own nature came back to me again. I cannot find the words to make you understand the great joy that filled my heart at finding myself a man again. I swam around for a little while, then I shouted at the top of my voice for someone to pull me out of the water. A rope was let down from the ship to me by someone I could not see, but I grabbed it and I was pulled aboard.

"There was no one on the ship but two young boys and their father. These were the Giant O'Dowd and his two sons, who were taking the air for themselves. At first they thought I was a thief who was coming to rob them and they started to attack me. I had to fight back to defend myself and the Giant O'Dowd fell by my hand. I sent his two sons home to their own country after this and I never heard another word about them since.

"When I searched the ship I found the Sword of Light, and until now I wouldn't part with it for silver or gold, even though many is the person who put the poison of his eye on it and wanted to get it from me, but there was no one tried harder to get it than my own brother, the Red Wizard. In order to live at peace and free from that crafty fellow, I made this Strong Fort to live in.

"I was so delighted with the change that came in my life that I went back to see my wife's father, the King of Greece, and to tell him the wrong that had been done to me. No sooner did I come before him than he welcomed me heartily, and my wife threw herself down on her two knees and asked my forgiveness. I took pity on her when she told me how she repented for what she had done, and for fear she would get any blame, or that anyone would try to punish her, I said I was willing to take her as my wife again. From that on there hasn't been a woman in the whole world better than she.

"And now you know who stole the Golden Boat and who killed the Giant O'Dowd, and you can take the Sword of Light with you and my blessing with it."

The farmer then said goodbye to the Youthful Warrior, and after spending a while with his wife's mother and father he turned his face towards home. A week before that the Red Wizard was struck down by a disease and he died, so now the farmer was able to keep the Sword of Light for himself. His wife welcomed him with great joy, and he thought she would smother him with kisses and drown him with tears until she dried him with towels of silk and satin.

They lived happily for the rest of their lives after that — as may be the lot of all of us.

Moireen

*T*HERE WAS a poor widow woman there long ago; it is often there was and there will be again. She had three daughters. Two of them were grown up to be young women. The third, who was called Moireen, was younger and smaller than the other two. Every day Moireen went out to herd the goats for her mother.

The mother loved Moireen much more than she did either of the others, and because of that they became angry and jealous of her, and when the mother was away from home they used to quarrel with her and bully her. The mother found this out, and it was the cause of much worry and anxiety to her, and when Moireen used to come home in the evening with her goats she used to see her mother crying. She thought in her own mind that they were giving her mother the same treatment as they were giving herself. Moireen and her mother were going through that trouble for a long time, so long that neither of them could remember the day when they had last got a civil word from the two.

The elder pair would like to see their mother dead, or out of the way somehow, and all because she loved Moireen more than she did them. So one day they made a plan to put her to death. For this purpose they filled a big caldron with water and put it down on the fire. The old woman asked them what they

wanted with all that water. They told her it was to wash
and clean her they wanted it, and then they caught her and
thrust the poor old woman into the caldron that was now boiling mad. They covered the pot then and left her there till the
blood and flesh melted off her bones, and then they took the
bones and hid them in a garden that was a little way down from
the house.

That was all very well till Moireen came home that evening
with the goats, and she saw no sign of her mother in the corner
by the fire, where she used to be, and she searched all around
the house, up and down, and she could not find a trace of her.

"Where is my mother?" she asked her sisters.

"We don't know at all," said they, "she went out there a while
ago to some place."

Moireen ate her supper then, and she went out afterwards to
search for her mother, but she could not find her high or low,
east, or west. She came in then and asked her sisters again
where her mother was. They said to her right out that they
neither knew nor cared where she was. Moireen started crying
and lamenting when she heard this, and she said that they
must have done something wrong to her mother. They said to
her then:

"If we did do something to her, maybe it is as well for you
to know, as we might do the same to you."

She was certain then from the way they were talking that
they had done away with her mother, and she began to search
every hole and corner again, until in the heel of the hunt she
found her bones where her sisters had hidden them, and had
no doubt at all in her mind that they were her mother's bones.

She put the little heap of bones then into her apron, and took
them down into the small garden that was at the back of the
house, and there she cried her fill over them. She put them

safely away there where nobody could see them, and there
was no day passed that she did not come there to cry her heart
out again. Then one day when she was grieving and lamenting
over them, and when she thought to put them back into their
hiding place again as she usually did, she looked down into her
apron at them, and what was there, instead of the bones, but a
little cat. That took a start out of her, but the little cat told
her not to have any fear, for she would do no harm to her,
but rather it was good she would do her.

"And now," said the little cat, "come along with me, for
you have no business staying here with your sisters from this
on, for maybe it is the way they would do you harm, as they
did to your mother."

They went off together then, herself and the little cat, until
they went a long way from home, and they came to the house
of a nobleman.

"Here now," said the little cat, "go up to that nobleman's
house and ask them to take you in as a servant girl, and take
whatever wages they will offer you, and the work they will
give you will be to clear the ashes and to look after the ducks.
And come here anytime you will need advice, and I will be
here before you, and anyway come here next Friday."

Moireen went off and she settled to be the girl to clear the
ashes and to mind the ducks in the nobleman's house. She
was busy every day doing her work, and she did it well. Everyone in the house liked her, especially the other servants, because she was always ready to help them when she had her own
work finished. When Friday came she went to meet the little
cat, and she was there before her, in the same place where they
had parted from each other the week before.

"And how do you like your place?" asked the little cat.

"I like it very well," said Moireen. "It is a fine place."

"Well," said the little cat, "there will be a fair near here tomorrow, and on every Saturday for the next two Saturdays, and it will be held inside in the big fairfield. All the household will go the fair tomorrow, and they will leave you to mind the house. A little while after leaving the stable yard, the young master will come back looking for his gloves that he had forgotten, and he will ask you to bring them to him. Let you get a nice, clean linen towel then, and take him the gloves in it, and come over here to me after that."

And that's how things happened. Moireen went home and went on with her business as usual, cleaning out the ashes and minding the ducks, until Saturday morning came. Then the people of the house started to get themselves ready to go to the fair, all except poor Moireen, and they all went off when they were ready. The young master had not long left the house when he came back and said he had forgotten his gloves.

"I forgot my gloves, Moireen, see if you could get them for me."

"I will, surely," said she. She went off then, and got a nice, clean linen towel; she put the gloves into it and she gave them to him. "Good girl, Moireen," he said, and he jumped up on his horse and away he went to the fair. When he had gone a little way from the house, Moireen went off to meet the little cat.

"Well now," said the cat, "did things happen as I said they would?"

"Yes, they did," said Moireen, "just the way you said."

"And did you do as I told you?" asked the little cat.

"I did," said Moireen.

The little cat came then and drew a rush out of a clump of rushes, and a beautiful dress appeared; it was as brilliant as the

rainbow, and when Moireen put it on it covered her from head
to foot. The little cat drew another rush out of the clump and it
changed into a beautiful brown steed, and that steed would overtake the wind in front of him and the wind behind him could
not catch up with him. The little cat told Moireen to get up on
the horse and that he would take her to the fair and back
here again without any guiding.

"Now," said the little cat, "make a round of the fairfield,
and when you are making for the gate coming back, the young
master will be standing there before you, and he will say to you:
'Kindly tell me where you are from, if you please.' You are to say
to him that you are from the Town of the Gloves, and come
home quickly after that."

And that is how it happened. Moireen got up on the horse
and she went to the fair. When she went into the fairfield
everyone began to look at her, and they were wondering who
in the world was the fine young lady. The young master especially was watching her while she was making a round of the fairfield and while she was heading for the gate on the way back.
He made no mistake at all about being at the gate before her,
and as she was passing him, he asked her:

"Kindly tell me where you are from, if you please."

"From the Town of the Gloves," said she, and off with her out
the gate.

The young master jumped on his horse to overtake her, so
as to get some more information from her, but if he did it was
little use for him, for she was gone out of sight by the time he
was in the saddle.

Moireen came home, and the little cat was there before her.
She asked Moireen if everything had gone as she said it would,
and Moireen said it had. The little cat took the horse and the

clothes from her, and she told her to put on her old clothes again, and not to let anyone know she had been at the fair at all.

And that is the way it was till the servants and the people of the house came home. The young master was very cast down because he had not been able to have any more talk with the beautiful young lady he had seen at the fair. The other servants came to Moireen and said to her:

"Ah Moireen, you missed a treat by not being at the fair today."

"Why did I?" asked Moireen.

"Ah," they said, "the finest and the most beautiful young woman that anyone ever saw was there today, and no one knows who she is or where she came from. And the young master never took his eyes off her, from the time she came into the fair till she left it."

"Is that so now?" said Moireen, and she very little interested in their talk.

"And Moireen," they went on, "you will have to go to the fair next Saturday, so that you may see her, if she comes. One of us will stay at home and mind the house instead of you."

"Indeed I won't go to the fair at all," said Moireen, "I have no mind at all to go there."

So far so good. Everyone was busy with his own work till Saturday came again. Moireen did not forget to go to the little cat on Friday.

"Well now," said the cat, "they will all go to the fair again tomorrow, and you will be left to mind the house. The young master will forget his spurs, and he will come back to the house for them. You do as you did last Saturday, and come here to me when he will have gone."

And just as the little cat said, they all went to the fair except Moireen. The young master had left the house only a short time when he found he had forgotten his spurs. He came back and said:

"Moireen, I forgot my spurs, see if you could get them for me, like a good girl."

"I will, and welcome," said Moireen, and she went and got a nice, clean linen towel, put the spurs in it and gave them to him. He went on then to the fair, and Moireen went to meet the little cat.

"Now," said the little cat, "did everything happen just as I said?"

"It happened just as you said," said Moireen.

"And did you do as I told you?" asked the little cat.

"I did," said Moireen.

"That's good," said the little cat. She went then to the clump of rushes, and she drew a rush out of it, and it turned into a beautiful dress, more beautiful than the one she had last Saturday. Then she drew another rush, and a brown steed came out of that. The little cat said to Moireen to jump on the steed and go off to the fair, and go around the fairfield once, "Just as you did last Saturday. And the young master will be at the gate before you again. He will ask you: 'Where are you from, if you please?' and you tell him that you are from the Town of the Spurs, and go on your road."

Moireen did as the little cat had told her, and for a while before she came in sight everyone in the fairfield had his eyes strained, watching for the beautiful lady who had been there on the Saturday before. But whatever person was watching out, or not watching out, the young master kept his two eyes carefully on the gate of the fairfield, to see her when she would come. It was not long until they saw her making towards the field, a still more beautiful young lady than the young lady of last Saturday. She rode once around the fairfield, and when she was facing the gate, on her way back, the young master made no mistake about being there before her.

"Where did you come from, if you please?" he asked her as she went through the gate.

"From the Town of the Spurs," she answered as she made off.

The young master hastened as much as he could to catch up with her and to get better acquainted, but it was little use for him, for there was no overtaking her.

Moireen came home with the speed of the wind. The little cat was there before her. She took the horse from Moireen, and the beautiful clothes, as she had done on the Saturday before. She told Moireen then not to pretend anything to anyone, but to go on doing her work as before, and to come back and meet her on the following Friday.

That was all very well till the servants came home from the fair. They ran up to Moireen and said:

"Oh Moireen, you lost it that you did not go to the fair to-day. The most beautiful lady, twice as beautiful as the one that came last Saturday, was there. You must come next Saturday, whether you like it or not, and one of us will stay behind and mind the house."

"Indeed, I will not," said Moireen; "wouldn't I be a nice sight at the fair with my ragged clothes, and do not be asking me to go, for it is no use for you."

They gave up asking her then when they saw she was so determined, and each and all went about his own work for the next week. And so it was till Friday came, and Moireen went to meet the little cat as usual. The little cat said to her that everything would happen again tomorrow as it happened last Saturday, but that this time it was his whip that the young master would forget. He would come back for it, and she was to bring it to him on a nice, clean linen towel, just as she had brought him the gloves and the spurs, and then she was to come to the little cat when he had gone.

Moireen went home then and did her work until Saturday morning came. All in the house went to the fair then. After a short time the young master came back for his whip, which he had forgotten.

"Moireen, see if you could find my whip for me, like a good girl," said he.

"I will and welcome," said Moireen. She went then and she got a nice, clean linen towel, as she had done before, and she put the whip into it, and brought it to him.

After that Moireen went to meet the little cat.

"Did you do everything as I told you?" asked the little cat.

"I did," said Moireen.

"That's good," said the cat. She went to the clump of rushes and drew a rush out of it, and it changed into a dress the color of the rainbow. She told Moireen to put the dress on her. The little cat drew another rush out of the clump of rushes, and that changed into a beautiful brown steed.

"Get up on the steed now and go to the fair," said the little cat. "Ride around the fairfield once, and when you will be making for the gate coming back, the young master will be there before you. He will ask you: 'Where are you from, if you please?' Say that you came from the Town of the Whip. He has made up his mind not to part from you today without getting a better account from you as to who you are. He will try to get a hold of your bridle; he will not succeed in that but he will catch your foot, and he will take your shoe with him in the attempt. Do not pay any heed to that, but come home as quickly as ever you can, and I will be here before you."

So far so good. Moireen went off on the steed, and when she went in on the fairfield every eye was on her. They all thought she was the finest woman they had ever seen, and especially the young master thought so. He never took his two eyes off her while she was riding around the field, and he made no mistake about being at the gate before her. He made up to her and said:

"Where are you from, if you please?"

"From the Town of the Whip," said she riding off.

But just as she was going through the gate, he tried to catch the bridle of her horse. He did not succeed in that, but instead of catching the bridle he caught her foot, and her shoe slipped off in his hand. He looked at the shoe and said to himself:

"I put myself under a bond not to marry any woman but the woman that this shoe will fit."

Moireen came home and the little cat was there before her.

"Did everything happen as I said?" she asked.

"Everything happened just as you said it would," said Moireen.

The little cat then took the clothes and the steed from her, just as she had done before, and she gave Moireen her old clothes. She put them on, went home and started her work.

That was all very well until the servants came home and ran up to Moireen saying: "Oh Moireen, you lost it not to be at the fair today."

"Why?" asked Moireen.

"Oh," said they, "the most beautiful woman that eye ever saw was there today, and when she was going out the gate the young master tried to catch the bridle of her horse, but he did not manage to do that, but he caught one of her shoes, and he has it now."

"Well then, I don't know what good that will do him," said

Moireen, going on with her work as if she were not a bit interested in the story.

On the following day the young master sent out a proclamation calling on all the young women around the place to come and try on the shoe and see if it would fit any of them, and saying that the first one it fitted, she would be the one he would marry. He named a certain day for them to come to his house. So all the young women around were getting ready for the appointed day; some were taking the tops off their big toes, and others were said to be taking slices off their heels. And when the day came a great crowd of young women were gathered there at early morning. Moireen hid herself in a big chest, as she was ashamed to be seen by the strangers in the ragged clothes which were all she had to wear.

As the day wore on all the young women had tried on the shoe, and there was no one there who could get her foot into it, it was so small, the little cat came and jumped up on the chest and said:

"Miaou, miaou, Moireen is hidden inside in this chest and the shoe will fit her nicely."

"Hit that miserable cat down out of that!" said one of the people of the house. Someone then struck the cat, and she jumped down.

After another while the cat jumped up on the chest again and said:

"Miaou, miaou, Moireen is under the lid of this chest and the shoe will fit her nicely."

"Hit down that wretch of a cat," said one of the crowd. Someone then gave the cat a blow, and she ran away into a corner.

A woman came then and tried on the shoe, and she, but as

little as the others, could not get her foot into it. The cat came out of the corner and jumped up on the lid of the chest and said:

"Miaou, miaou, Moireen is in the chest and the shoe will fit her nicely."

"Hit that fairy of a cat down," said one of the people of the house.

"Indeed, do not hit her," said the nobleman. "I have been listening to that cat for a while now, and I think that maybe she is right. Let Moireen be brought here so that she may try on the shoe."

The lid of the chest was raised and Moireen came out.

"Come here, Moireen," said the young master, "try this shoe on you."

Moireen was very shy as she tried on the shoe, because she was ashamed of her ragged clothes before so many strangers, but no sooner did she put her foot into the shoe than it slipped on her as if it were made for her. Everyone was very surprised that it was Moireen that the shoe fitted, and many of them were jealous enough of her.

"Now, Moireen," said the young nobleman, "you are the one I am going to marry, and I make you a present of this shoe."

He turned to the other young women then and said: "Go off home with yourselves now."

On the following morning the young master asked Moireen to come with him and they would get married.

"Wait now," said she. "I have to get myself ready. It isn't in these old rags you think I would go to be married."

"I didn't know you had any other clothes," said the nobleman.

"I have a few others that I think will look better on me," said Moireen.

She went off with herself then to the little cat, and she took the shoe with her.

"Now," said the little cat, "so you're going to be married."

"I am," said Moireen.

"That you may have every kind of luck," said the cat. "And I am very glad that you will be settled so comfortably," and with that she went to the clump of rushes.

She drew a rush out of it and the beautiful dress appeared, the one that Moireen had worn on the Saturday before, that was of the colors of the rainbow. She told Moireen to put on the clothes, and she did. The little cat went to the clump of rushes again, she drew another rush out of it, and that turned into a beautiful brown steed.

"And now, Moireen," said the little cat, "do you know who I am?"

"I am not sure that I do," said Moireen.

"I am your mother," said the little cat, "and you will not see me any more from today on. But maybe I will be able to give you help without your knowing it. And I will leave you two gifts before I go from you. The first is that your fingers will shed honey every single day, and the second is that the birds of the air will sing their songs for you, wherever you are. And you can keep as a present that brown steed and the beautiful dress."

She told Moireen then to get up on the horse quickly, and ride off to the house of the nobleman, "For he is waiting for you by this time," she said.

The little cat then gave her a blessing and said goodbye, and Moireen left a blessing with the little cat too.

She rode off on the brown steed then, and she found that the young nobleman was waiting for her. When he saw her coming his eyes nearly jumped out of his head with surprise, for he had no idea that Moireen was the woman from whom he had taken the shoe on the day of the fair until he saw her again wearing the same clothes and riding on horseback. It was then he recalled the answer the lady had given him at the gate of the fairfield when he asked her where she had come from; she had said from "the Town of the Gloves," "the Town of the Spurs," "the Town of the Whip," on each of the three Saturdays, when he had forgotten his gloves, then his spurs and then his whip. Now he knew that it was Moireen who had been there all the time, and it was he that was the happy man.

They went off and they got married. They came home and they lived very happily for the greater part of a year, until the sisters heard that Moireen was married. They were very envious of her. They went to live near her, and that was not for Moireen's good.

All was going well then till Moireen fell sick and sent word to her sisters. The eldest one came and sent for a midwife. When the midwife came the nobleman said to his wife's sister that he would stay outside on the lawn, strolling around, until they would send for him.

A fine young son was born to Moireen. Moireen's sister said to the midwife that she was to kill the child some way or other, and she bribed her to say that the child was born dead. The sister went out then to the young nobleman and he asked her what news she had for him.

"I have good news," said she, "only the child is dead."

"Oh, that's not too bad," said he. "I do not mind about the child so much as long as my wife is well. Let the child be taken and buried in some place nearby."

The sister went back then and she took the child, unknown to anyone, and threw it into the sea. The nobleman's house was quite close to the sea.

The sister went back to her own house at the end of a week

after that. Moireen was very sad that the child was dead, but her husband told her not to fret on that score, but instead to be thankful that her own health was so good.

After a while Moireen fell sick again. The sister made no mistake about coming again, and she sent for the midwife once more. Another son was born to Moireen, and the sister bribed the midwife to do what she had done before, and say that the child was born dead. The young nobleman stayed out on the lawn waiting for news, as he had done the first time. His sister-in-law came out to him, and he asked her what news she had. She said that she had good news but that the child was dead. He said that it was good news, and that he did not mind about the loss of the child so much as long as his wife was well. "And," said he, "let the child be taken and buried in some little corner." Then Moireen's sister went back to the house and, unknown to everyone, she took the child and threw it into the sea.

When Moireen was well again the sister went off to her own house. Everything went well for a while till Moireen fell sick again, and the sister made no mistake about coming back once more. To make a long story short, the sister and the midwife did the same thing as they had done before, and the third child was thrown into the sea in the same way as were the other two. When the nobleman was told that the child was dead, it did not surprise him; he said there was no help for it, and that he did not mind so much about the child so long as his wife was well.

When the sister saw that she could not make trouble between Moireen and her husband she made a plan in her own mind. She stayed on in the house for a week until Moireen was up out of bed and as well as ever, or nearly so. Then one day the sister said to Moireen:

"Come on out with me and we'll go walking by the sea. It will do your health good."

"Indeed I would like that," said Moireen.

They went off down to the sea then. They walked by the edge of a high cliff. The sister came on the inside of Moireen, gave her a push with her shoulder and threw her into the sea. She ran back to the nobleman's house and ran in clapping her hands and lamenting.

"What's wrong with you?" asked the nobleman.

Panting and excited, she answered him: "Oh, Moireen and I — were walking — by the sea — along the top — of the cliff — we were looking into — the sea. A cloud — came over — her vision — or something — like it — in such a way — that —she fell into — the sea!"

The nobleman and his household ran as quickly as they could down to the cliff. They got skiffs and boats and searched every nook and cranny, hole and corner in the sea at the foot of the cliff, but not a trace of Moireen could they find, dead or alive. They had to come home in the end, and the nobleman was truly miserable and brokenhearted about the loss of his wife.

The sister went home to her own house then, and she was well satisfied that the plan she had made to put an end to Moireen had succeeded so well. Time passed, and bit by bit the nobleman's sorrow passed too, and he began to think that it would be better for him to get married again. So he sent for the sister who used to be waiting on Moireen, and he asked her would she be willing to marry him. She said she would surely, if for no other reason but for the great love and affection she had for Moireen. They were married then and he brought her home with him.

So far so good. Everything went well, and very well for a few days. But about that time a servant boy, whom the nobleman had working for him, was walking along by the edge of the sea, and looking down into the sea he saw a woman with a child at her breast, and having two other children with her, and they were playing around in the sea for themselves. The servant boy was greatly astonished when the woman spoke to him and said:

"O boy, the best servant that anyone ever had, tell me, do the fingers of your mistress shed honey every day, and do the birds sing their songs for her wherever she goes?"

"The fingers of my mistress do not drip honey," said he, "nor do the birds sing their songs for her."

And before he had time to say another word, the woman and the children had gone out of his sight. He went off home then and he told his master what he had seen and what the woman had said to him.

"Ah, have sense, boy, you must be raving," said his master.

On the following day the boy took the same path over the cliff. Again he saw the woman and the children in the same place where they were the day before. The woman put the same question to him about his mistress, and the servant boy gave her the same answer. Then the woman and the children disappeared. He went off home then and he told his master again what he had seen, and he told him:

"That woman is the dead spit of Moireen."

"Ah, shut your mouth and have sense, you foolish fellow," said his master.

The servant boy went back to the same place the third day, and he walked by the edge of the sea where he had seen the woman and the three children on the two previous days. Looking down into the sea he saw them again. The woman spoke to him and she put the same question to him once more. He answered her just as he had on the two other days. He came home then and he told his master what he had seen and what the woman had said to him, "And," said he, "I would swear on my oath that it was Moireen was there."

"Indeed," said his master, "maybe you did see something, so I will go with you myself tomorrow, to the place where you said you have seen this woman and the three children."

And right enough he went, and he saw them. And he saw at one glance that it was Moireen that was there. When she saw him she welcomed him. He got a boat then, and he went on the sea, and he took Moireen and his three sons out of the sea into the boat with him.

On the way home he asked Moireen how it was that she wasn't drowned, and if those were the three children that he was told were dead when they had come into the world.

"They are your three children, and they were not born dead," she said. "And I have a long story to tell you about them and about many other things, but I will tell it to you some other time."

"I will not stir a foot until you tell me," said he. "You must tell me everything now."

She began on her story then, and she told it to him from beginning to end. She told him how her sisters used to treat her when she was at home with them, about the death they gave her mother, and she told him all about the little cat. "And," she said, "my sisters' ill-will always followed me to the very end when one of them threw me over the cliffs into the sea."

"Stop!" said he. "What's that you said? Your sister threw you into the sea?"

"Ah, then, she did," said Moireen, "and my three sons before me, and they were alive and —"

"Oh! Oh!" said he. "Wait here awhile. I won't be a minute,"

and he made towards the house. Moireen said, in her own mind:

"He's in a raging temper now, and maybe he'll do something wrong."

When he went into the house he gave orders to have the sister tied up and thrown into the sea from the same cliff from which she had thrown Moireen. He gave orders to get the other sister and to do the same thing with her, for fear she might do some further harm, and his orders were carried out. He went back then and brought his wife and his three children home with him.

It was not long till the story of Moireen and her three sons spread all around the countryside, and when the midwife heard of the death that Moireen's two sisters got, no one ever saw her, dead or alive, near the place after that.

Moireen and the nobleman lived happily from that out, without any trouble or anxiety of any kind. He never grew tired of listening to Moireen's story of how she and her sons lived in the sea.

Shawn MacBreogan and the King
of the White Nation

THERE WAS a very rich man once who lived near Brandon Bay,
and his name was Breogan.

This Breogan had a deal of fine land, and was well liked by
all the people who knew him. One morning as he was walking
on the strand for himself, he found, above the highest tide,
a little colt, barely the size of a goat; and a very nice colt he
was.

"Oh, what a beautiful little beast!" said Breogan. "He doesn't
belong to anyone in this country. He is not mine; but still and
all I'll take him. If an owner comes the way, sure he can prove
his claim, if he is able."

Breogan carried the colt to the stable, and fed him as well as
any beast he had. The colt was thriving well; and when twelve
months were passed, it was a pleasure to look at him. Breogan
put him in a stable by himself after that, and kept him three
years. At the end of the third year, it isn't a little colt he was,
but a grand fiery steed. Breogan invited all his friends and
neighbors to a feast and a great merrymaking. "This will be a
good time," thought he, "to find a man to ride the strange
colt."

There was a splendid racecourse on the seashore. The appointed day came, and all the people were assembled. The horse was brought out, bridled and saddled, and led to the strand. The place was so crowded that a pin falling from the sky would not fall on any place but the head of some person old or young, some man, woman, or child that was there at the festival.

For three days the women of the village were cooking food for all that would come; there was enough ready, and to spare. Breogan strove to come at a man who would ride the horse; but not a man could he find. The horse was so fiery that all were in dread of him.

Not to spoil sport for the people, Breogan made up his mind to ride himself. As soon as the man mounted and was firm in the saddle, the horse stood on his hind legs, rose with a leap in the air, and away with him faster than any wind, first over the land, and then over the sea. The horse never stopped till he came down on his forefeet in *Breasil*, which is part of *Tir na n-Og* (the Land of the Young).

Breogan found himself now in the finest country man could set eyes on. He rode forward, looking on all sides with delight and pleasure, till out before him he saw a grand castle, and a beautiful gate in front of it, and the gate partly open.

"Well," thought he, "I'll go in here for a bit, to know are there people living inside."

With that he tied the bridle to one of the bars of the gate and left the horse, thinking to come back in a short time. He went to the door of the castle and knocked on it. A woman came out and opened the door to him.

"Oh, then, a hundred thousand welcomes to you, Breogan from Brandon," said she.

He thanked her, and was greatly surprised when he heard her calling him by name. She brought him then to a parlor; and, though he had fine rooms in his own house, he hardly knew at first how to sit in the parlor, it was that grand and splendid. He wasn't long sitting when who should come in but a young woman, a beauty; the like of her he had never seen before in his life. She was first in every way, in good looks as well as in manners. She sat down at his side and welcomed him.

Breogan remained in the castle a few hours, eating, drinking, talking, and enjoying himself. At long last he thought: "I must be going"; and then he said so.

The woman laughed.

"Well, now, my good friend," said she, "of all the men that ever came to this place — and it's many a man that came here in my time — there never was a worse man to care for his horse than what you are. Your poor beast is tied to a bar of the gate outside since you came, and you have never as much as thought he was dry or hungry; and if I had not thought of him, it's in a bad state he'd be now. How long do you think you are in this castle?"

"Oh, then, I'm about seven hours in it."

"You are in this country just seven years," said the woman. "The beauty and comfort of this Land of the Young is so great that the life of twelve months seems the length of one hour in another place."

"If I'm here that long, I must be going this minute," said Breogan.

"Well," said the woman, "if you are going, I must ask you one question. There will be a child in this castle; and you are the father, 'tis you that should name it. Now what will the name be?"

"If 'tis a son, you'll call him Shawn, the son of Breogan, from Brandon in Erin. You'll rear him for seven years. At the end of that time give him your blessing and the means of making a

journey to Erin. Tell him who I am; and if he is anything of a
hero, he'll not fail to make me out."

Breogan left his blessing with the woman, went to the gate,
and found his horse standing there, tied in the same way that he
left him. He untied the beast, mounted, and away through the air
with him, leaving *Breasil* behind him, and never stopped nor
halted till he came down about a mile from his own house, near
Brandon, exactly seven years from the day he left it. Seeing on
the strand a great number of people, he wondered why they
were in it, and what brought them together. A large, fine-looking
man was passing the way, and Breogan called out to him.

"What are these people all doing that I see on the strand?" he
asked.

"You must be a stranger," said the man, "not to know what
these people are here for."

"I'm no stranger," said Breogan, "but I went out of the country a few years before this, and while I was gone there were
changes."

"If a man leaves his own country for a short time itself," said
the other, "he will find things changed when he comes back
again to it. I will tell you why these people are here. We had
in this place a fine master, and it's good and kind he was to us.
He went out to the strand one day, walking, and found a little
colt above the high tide. He took the colt home, reared and fed
him three years. Then this man gathered the people to give them
a feast, and to know could he find someone to ride the horse.
When no one would venture, he mounted himself; and all saw
how the horse rose in the air, made a leap over the harbor, and
then away out of sight. We think that he fell and was drowned
in the sea; for neither Breogan nor the horse was ever seen
after. We are sorry for the man, because he was kind to us; but

'tis equal what became of the horse. After waiting seven years, Breogan's wife is to be married this evening to some great man from the north. We don't know what kind he is. He may destroy us, or drive us out of our houses."

Breogan thanked the man for his words, and hurried on towards his own house. The servants saw him coming, knew him, and cried: "Here comes the master!" and there was a great stir up and down in the house. Next minute the wife heard the news; and out she ran to meet her husband. Any man would think she was glad to see Breogan.

"Why are all the people here today?" asked he of the wife.

"And was it not this day seven years that you put the country behind you, wherever you went? You left dinner here ready; and the dinner is in the same state it was the day you went away from me. I thought it better to send for the people again, and eat the dinner in memory of you that prepared it."

The husband said nothing. The people ate the dinner; and every man, woman, and child went home satisfied.

At the end of another seven years Breogan made a great dinner again. All was ready; a great crowd of people were present. The day being fine, you could see far in every direction.

"Look now," said Breogan, to one of his men who had very good eyesight. "Look out towards the water, to know can you see anything coming. Seven years ago today I came home from *Breasil,* in the Land of the Young; and my son, if I have one, is to be here today. He ought to be coming by this time."

The man looked out as well as he could.

"I see a boat with one mast coming towards us," said he, "and it's sailing faster than any boat I ever set eyes on. In the boat I can see only one young man, and very young he is too."

"Oh, that is he," said Breogan.

The boat came in at full sail, and it wasn't long till the youth was standing before his father.

"Who are you?" asked Breogan.

"My name is Shawn MacBreogan."

"If that is your name, sit down here at dinner, for you are my son."

When the feast was over the people went home. When Breogan's wife found out who the boy was, she wouldn't give the breadth of a ha'penny piece of his body for a fortune, she was that fond of him.

Things went on well till one day when Breogan and his son were out hunting. The day being warm, they sat down to rest, and the son said to the father:

"Since I came to you in Erin, you seem vexed in yourself. I have not asked what trouble is on you, or is there anything amiss with you."

"All things are well with me but one thing," said Breogan. "There is some understanding between my wife and a man in the north of Erin. I am in dread of my life, for while I was in *Breasil* she saw this man, and the day I came home they were going to be married. Since then I have not slept soundly in bed, for messages are passing between them."

"Very well, Father, I'll put an end to that soon," said Shawn. He rose on the following morning, caught his hurley in his right hand, and his ball in the left. He threw up the ball, then struck it with the hurley, and was driving it that way before him till he reached the north of Erin, and never let his ball touch the ground even one time. He inquired for his father's opponent. When he found out the house, he knocked at the door.

"Is your master inside?" asked he.

"He is," said the servant.

"Go," said Shawn, "and tell him that I want him, and not to delay, as I must be at dinner in Brandon this evening."

The master of the house came out, and, seeing a boy there before him, thought it strange that he should speak rudely to a man like himself.

"If you don't beg my pardon this minute, I'll take the head off you," said the man.

"Well," said Shawn, "I'm not here to beg pardon of you or of any man; but I came to have satisfaction for the trouble you put on my father, and I far away from him."

"Who is your father?"

"My father is Breogan of Brandon."

Out the man went; and the two stood on a fine green plain and began to fight with swords, cutting each other's flesh. They were not long at the swords when Shawn said:

"It's getting late, and I must be at home before dinner today, as I promised; there is no use in delay."

With that he rose out of his body and gave the man a blow between the head and the shoulders that put the head a mile away from the body. Shawn caught the head before it touched the earth; then, grasping it by the hair, he left the body where it fell, took his hurley in his right hand, threw his ball in the air, and drove it far to the south with the hurley; and he drove it across Erin in that way, the ball never touching ground from the far north of Erin to Brandon. Holding the ball and hurley in his hand, he went into the house and laid the head at his father's feet.

"Now, my dear Father," said he, "here is the head of your enemy; he'll trouble you no more from this out."

When Breogan's wife saw the head, she was cut to the heart and troubled, though she would not let any man know it. One day when the father and son came home from killing ducks, she was groaning and said she was ready to die.

"Is there any cure for you here or in the world?" asked Shawn.

"There is no getting the cure that would heal me; there is no cure but three apples from the white orchard in the White Nation."

"Well," said the boy, "I promise you not to eat the third meal at the one table, nor sleep the second night in the one bed, till I get the three apples from the White Nation."

The father was very angry when they came out of the bedroom. "Sure," said he, "it would be enough for you to risk your life for your own mother."

"Well, I must go now," said Shawn; "the promise is given; I'll not break my word."

So away with him on the following morning; and on that day's journey he came to a glen, and in it was a house. In the house there was no living creature but a white mare with nine eyes.

"A hundred thousand welcomes to you, Shawn MacBreogan from Brandon. You must be tired and hungry after the day's journey," cried the mare. "Go in now to the next room and take supper and strengthen yourself."

He went into the next room, and inside in it was a table, and on the table was everything that the best king could wish for. He ate, drank, and went then and gave a hundred thousand thanks for the supper. He stood near the fire for a while; then the mare said:

"Come here and lie under my head; wonder at nothing you see, and let no word out of you."

He did as the mare said. About dusk three seals came in, and went to the supper room. They threw off their sealskins, and became three as fine young men as one could look at.

"I wish Shawn MacBreogan from Brandon were here tonight. I'd be glad to see him, and give him a present, and have his good company," said one of the three.

"I'd be glad to see him too," said the second, "and I'd give him a present."

"So would I," said the third.

"Go to them now," said the mare. "Enjoy their company. In the morning you'll ask for the presents."

He went out among them.

"A hundred thousand welcomes to you, Shawn MacBreogan," cried the young men. "And 'tis glad we are to see you."

They drank wine then, sang songs, and told tales, and never slept a wink all the night. Before sunrise they went as seals; and when going Shawn said:

"I hope you will not forget the presents you promised last evening."

"We will not," said the eldest. "Here is a cloak for you. While it is on you, you'll be the finest man in the world to look at."

"Here is a ball," said the second. "If you throw it in the air, and wish for anything you like, you will have it before the ball comes to the ground."

The third gave a whistle.

"When you blow this," said he, "every enemy that hears it will lie down asleep, and be powerless; and, besides, you're to have the white mare to ride."

He took the gifts.

"Give me a feed of grain before we start," said the mare. "No man has sat on me without being turned into froth and blown away, or else thrown and killed."

Shawn mounted her then, and she tossed him. She threw him very far the first time. He was badly shocked, but recovered. The second and the third times it was easier. The fourth time he mounted for the journey. It was not long till he came to the sea-shore. On the third day he was in sight of land in the White Nation. The mare ran over the water, and swiftly, without trouble; no bird ever went at such a speed.

When Shawn came near the castle, he stopped before a house at the edge of the town and asked a lodging of the owner, an old man.

"I'll give you that," said the old man, "and welcome, and a place for your horse."

After supper Shawn told his errand.

"I pity you," said the man. "I'm in dread you'll lose your life; but I'll do what I can for you. No man has ever been able to get one of those apples; and if a stranger is caught making up to them, the king takes his head without mercy or pardon. There is no kind of savage beast in the world but is guarding the apples; and there is not a minute in the night or day when some of the beasts are not watching."

"Do you know what virtue is in the apples?" asked Shawn.

"I do well," said the old man; "and it is I that would like to have one of them. If a man is sick, and eats even one bite of an apple, he'll be well; if old, he'll grow young again, and never know grief from that out; he will always be happy and healthy. I'll give you a pigeon to let loose in the orchard; she will go flying from one tree to another till she goes to the last one. All the beasts will follow her; and while they are hunting the pigeon, you will take what you can of the apples; but I hope you will not think it too much to give one to me."

"Never fear," said Shawn, "if I get one apple you'll have the half of it; if two, you'll have one of them."

The old man was glad. Next morning at daybreak Shawn took the pigeon, mounted the mare, and away with him to the orchard. When the pigeon flew in, and was going from tree to tree with a flutter, the beasts started after her. Shawn sprang in on the back of the mare, left her, and went to climb the first tree that he met for the apples; but the king's men were at him before he could touch a single apple, or go back to the mare. They caught him, and took him to the king. The mare sprang over the wall and ran to the house of the old man. Shawn told the king his whole story, said that his father was Breogan of Brandon, and his mother the Princess of *Breasil* in the Land of the Young.

"Oh," said the king, "you are the hero that I am waiting for this long time. A fine part of my kingdom is that island beyond; but 'tis taken by a giant who holds it with an army of hirelings. Clear that island of the giant and his men, bring me his head, and you'll have the apples."

Shawn went to the old man, then to the mare, and told her.

"You can do that without trouble," said she. "You have the power needed to do it."

Shawn took his breakfast, then sat on the mare and rode towards the island. Just before the mare touched the land, Shawn sounded the whistle; and everyone who heard it was asleep the next instant. Shawn took his sword then, swept the head off the giant, and before evening there wasn't a man alive on the island except Shawn himself. He tied the giant's head to the saddlebow, mounted the mare, and was ready to start, when she spoke to him:

"Be careful not to look back toward the island till you come down from my back."

With that she swept on, and soon they were nearing the castle. While crossing the yard, Shawn thought, "I have the island cleared; the head is safe on me; the apples are mine." With that he forgot the mare's words and turned to look back at the island; but as he did, he fell from the saddle, and where should he fall but down on a dust heap. A son of the comb-woman, a youth who fed dogs and small animals, was lying there at the time, and he sickly and full of sores. Shawn's cloak slipped from his shoulders and fell on this dirty, foul fellow; that moment he sprang up the finest-looking man in the king-dom. He fastened the cloak on his shoulders, mounted the white mare, and rode to the castle. The king was that glad when he looked at the head of the giant that he didn't know where to put the counterfeit hero who brought it.

"How did you clear the island?" asked the king. "And was it a hard task to take the head off the giant?"

"Oh, then," said the dogfeeder, "there was never such a battle in the world as the battle today on that island between the giant and myself and his forces; and 'tis well I earned what will come to me."

"You'll get good pay," said the king. "I promised you apples from my white orchard; but I'll give you more, I'll give you my youngest daughter in marriage, and that island for her portion. My daughter will not be of age to marry for a year and a day. Till that time is out you'll live with me here in this castle."

Believe me, the dogfeeder was a great man in his own mind that evening.

There was one woman in the yard who saw the deception, and that was the henwife. She knew well what the dogfeeder was, and 'tis often she said:

"He's the greatest liar on earth, and kind mother for him."

She drew Shawn into her own house, and he sick and full of sores, just like the dogfeeder, not a man in the world would have known him. She nursed and tended Shawn. On the sixth day he was able to speak; but he lay in great weakness, and covered with sores.

"How am I to be cured?" asked he of the henwife.

"I know," answered she. "I spoke to a wise woman today and got the right cure for you."

With that the henwife went down to a spring that belonged to the king's youngest daughter, and pulled up nine rushes growing near it. Three of these she threw away, and kept six of them. She cut the white from the green parts, crushed them in water, gave Shawn some of the water to drink, and rubbed the rest on his body. A week was not gone when he was as sound and as well as ever.

Shawn heard now the whole story of the dogfeeder's lies and prosperity. He took service himself in the castle; and a few days after that the king gave a hunt, and invited all the guests in the castle to go with him. Shawn had to go as a basketboy, and carry provisions like any servant. Toward evening, when the company was on a wild moor twenty miles from the castle, a thick mist fell, and all were afraid that their lives would be gone from them.

"I can take you to a castle," said Shawn.

"Take us," said the king.

"I will if you give me your daughter to marry."

"She is promised to another," said the king.

"I have the best right to her," said Shawn. "It was I that cleared the island."

"I don't believe you," said the king.

"We'll be lost, every man of us," said the chief hunter. "Give him the promise, he may be dead before the day of the wedding."

The king gave his promise. The basketboy stepped behind a great rock, threw up the ball, and wished for the finest castle on earth. Before the ball touched the ground, the king, the guests, and attendants were in a castle far finer than any they had looked on in daylight or seen in a dream. The best food and drink of all kinds were in it, shining chambers and beds of silk and gold. When all had eaten and drunk their fill, they fell asleep to sweet music, and slept soundly till morning. At daybreak each man woke up and found himself lying on the wild moor, a tuft of rushes under his head, and the gray sky above him. Glad to see light, they rose and went home.

Now the henwife told the king's daughter the story of Shawn, who had cleared out the island, and the comb-woman's son, the deceiver. When the year was ended, and the day came for the marriage, the king's daughter said she would marry no man but the man who would ride the white mare with nine eyes (the mare could either kill or make froth of a man). The comb-woman's son was the first man to mount; but the cloak fell from him, and he vanished in froth blown away by the wind, and no one saw sight of him from that day to this. Sixteen kings' sons tried to ride the white mare, and were killed every man of them; but their bodies were found. Shawn, who had taken the cloak, sat on the mare, and rode three times past the castle. At the door the mare knelt for him to come down.

The king's daughter would have jumped through her window and killed herself, if her maids had not held her. She rushed down the stairs, kissed Shawn, and embraced him. The wedding began then. It lasted for a day and a year, and the last was the best day of all.

When the wedding was over, Shawn remembered the mare and went to the stable. She had not been fed, and a white skin was all that was left of her. When Shawn came to the mare's place, three young men and two women were playing chess in it.

"Oh, I forgot the mare from the first day of the wedding till this moment," said Shawn, and he began to cry.

"Why are you crying?" asked the elder of the two women.

He told the reason.

"You needn't cry," said the woman. "I can revive her." With that she took the skin, put it on herself; and that minute she was the white mare.

"Would you rather see me as a white mare, or the woman that I was a minute ago?"

"The woman," said Shawn.

She took off the skin and was a woman again. She told him then how the king, her father, made three seals of her brothers and a white mare of herself, to be in those forms till a hero should come who could clear out the island.

"You cleared the island," said she, "and we are all free again."

The king gave the island to his son-in-law, and as many apples from the orchard as he wished. The first thing that Shawn did was to take an apple to the old man who gave him lodgings when he came to the White Nation. At the first bite he swallowed, the old man was twenty-one years of age, young and hearty, and so happy that it would do any man good to have one look at him.

Shawn and his young wife lived another day and a year with her father, and then they went to visit his father in Brandon. From pretending to be sick, Breogan's wife became sick in earnest, and died. Breogan himself was now old and dissatisfied.

"The least I can do," thought Shawn, "is to give him an apple."

He gave him the apple. Breogan ate it, was twenty-one years of age; and if ever a man was glad in Erin, 'twas he was.

Shawn left the father young and happy at Brandon, and went back himself with his wife to the island.

The King's Son Who
Would Not Obey

*T*HERE WAS a king there long ago, and long ago it was, and he gathered together whatever riches were in the kingdom for himself, for he was truly greedy. He had six children—three boys and three girls—and it came to his knowledge that they all wished to be married. He was greatly troubled at hearing this, as he did not know where he would get the money for wedding feasts and dowries for them.

There was an old blind man in the kingdom who had the name of being wise. Blind John was his name. The king went to him to get advice on how he should get his children married, without spending too much money. Blind John said he would have to have three days and three nights to think about it, and that he would be able to eat only three mouthfuls of bread, and drink three drops of water, every day of the three days. And he said too, that he would have to lock himself up in a room, where no one would come near him for the three days.

Blind John did this, and on the third day he came to the king.

"Now," he said, "there is no woman in the country rich enough for any of your three sons. And there is no man in the country rich enough for your daughters. And if you scatter your wealth on these weddings, you and your wife will be left miserably poor, so my advice to you is to marry your children, one to the other, and that will keep your wealth in the family always.

The king said that what Blind John said was true, and that he would follow his advice. He called for his eldest son and his eldest daughter then, and they agreed to do what their father told them. He called for the second son and the second daughter, and they also said that they would do as their father bade them. Then the third son and the third daughter were brought before the king, their father, but the third son would not yield to his father's wish, on any account, and he refused to take such bad advice.

"Unless you will do my bidding," said the king, "I will put you and your sister, head foremost, out the door."

The son said he did not care, and the king then banished him and his sister from the palace. They started out then to seek their fortune, and they walked on and on, all day, until the night began to come down around them. The evening turned stormy, with great blustering winds and heavy rain. By this time they had come to a dark wood, and they were cold and hungry. They did not know where they would get a bite or a sup or a lodging for the night. The young girl began to cry and complain, and she said it would be better for them to turn back home, and do their father's bidding, as their two brothers and sisters had done.

The king's son said he would never do that, no matter what hardship he would suffer. Looking ahead of him then, he saw a light in the middle of the wood, so they started off and went towards it. When they drew near, they saw a big house there. The king's son went in and asked for lodgings for the night.

There were an old woman and an old man sitting by the fire. The old man said they could stay there and welcome.

"My sister is with me," said the king's son, "and unless I get lodging for her too, I will not stay."

"You will get lodging for her also," said the old man.

The king's son brought his sister in then, and they both sat down by the fire. The old man ordered his servant to make supper for them. When they had eaten their supper, they sat down by the fire again, and the old man asked the youth who they were, for it seemed to him that they had been well reared.

The king's son said that indeed they had been well reared, and very well reared, and then he told him what had happened to them, and why they had been banished from home.

"If your story is true," said the old man, "you are well fixed here, for I am a noble lord. I am wealthy and I have a good deal of land. If you will stay with me I will leave you my wealth and my lands when I die. And my wife has great riches too, and she will leave them to your sister." The king's son said he was very thankful to him, and that he would stay with him. They all went to bed then, and they got up on the following morning, and they ate a good breakfast.

"Come with me now," said the nobleman, "till I show you my place, as I would not like to keep you if you did not like the kind of living you would have with me."

They went out then to look around the nobleman's lands, and the king's son was pleased with all he saw.

"Now," said the nobleman, "all my tenants will be gathered here tomorrow to draw my turf home from the bog. I want you to take this little white dog and go into the field, over yonder, and set him at that flock of sheep that is grazing there. They will not run far till the fattest ram will fall, and he will be choked in his own fat. Bring him home then, and we will make a feast for my tenants."

It was true for him, for that is how it happened. The king's

son took the little white dog with him and he went into the
field. He set the dog at the flock of sheep, and he had not gone
far after them when the fattest ram fell down, and choked in
his own fat. The young man was bending down to take the
ram when he saw a maiden coming towards him, and she had
three dogs with her. She saluted the king's son and said: "You
would do well to give me that ram, and I will give you one of
these dogs. This dog's name is Heavy-Load, and he is that strong
that he can carry any load, no matter how heavy it may be; he
will be very useful to you later on."

The king's son refused to give her the ram, saying: "I am
a stranger in this place. I came here only last night, and perhaps
my master would not be satisfied to give the ram in exchange
for the dog."

But the young woman kept on begging him, and in the end
he gave her the ram for the strong dog.

The king's son set the small white dog at the flock the second
time, and again it was not long until the fattest ram fell, and
choked in his own fat.

The young woman came again, and said that it would be
better for him to give her that ram too, and she would give him
another dog, whose name was Swift. The dog Swift was so quick,
she told him, that he could overtake anything that would rise up
before him, bird or beast, and that he would be of great use
to him later on.

The king's son said that his master might not be pleased if he
made that exchange, but again, she pleaded so hard with him that
he gave her the ram for the dog Swift.

Then he set the small white dog at the flock for the third
time, and it was not long till the fattest ram fell, and choked in
his own fat.

"It is as well for you to give me that ram too," said the young woman, "and I will give you the third dog for him. This is a female dog, and her name is All-Knowing. She has so much knowledge and wisdom that she knows everything that is happening, not only in this country, but in every country in the world. And, what is more, the other dogs will be no good to you unless this dog is with them, and they will all be very useful to you in a little while."

In the end she got him to exchange the third ram for the dog called All-Knowing.

When he went back to the castle, the nobleman was outside waiting for him. The king's son told him what had happened, and that he had given away the three fattest rams in the flock.

"If you did," said the nobleman, "and if you made a good bargain, it is yourself that will benefit from it; but if it was a bad bargain you made, it is yourself too that will be at a loss by it, so I'm satisfied."

On the following morning the nobleman's tenants gathered and spent the day drawing the turf home from the bog, up to his door. In the evening the nobleman had a feast for them.

On the day after the feast the king's son said to the nobleman that he would like to go hunting in the woods, if he would be so good as to give him a loan of his gun.

"I do not like you to go into that wood," said the nobleman, "as I had seven sons, and they were all lost in that wood."

In spite of all that, the king's son said he would like to go there for a day's hunting. He said he was accustomed to do a lot of hunting, and he was not afraid of anything in the world.

And so it was. He went into the wood, with his gun and his three dogs. As he went along he kept meeting flocks of the finest game birds that anyone ever saw. After a while he began to shoot them, and he kept on shooting until he had a heap as high as a haystack. Then the strong dog, Heavy-Load, tossed them up on his back to take them home.

The nobleman was outside waiting for the young man when he came back. And he was so glad to see him back, safe and sound, that he ran to meet him. They had some of the birds plucked there and then, and they had a great feast of every kind of game bird for their supper.

On the following morning the king's son went off to the wood again, with his gun and his three dogs. As great as was the number of birds that he met the first day, he met three times as many on the second day. He kept firing his gun at them, till he had two heaps of birds, as high as two haystacks. He ordered the dog, Heavy-Load, to throw them up on his back and carry them home, and he did, and it was no trouble to him.

The nobleman was out waiting for him again that day, and when he saw him coming he ran with delight to welcome him. This time he had so many birds with him that it was more than the nobleman's household could do to eat them all in three months.

When the king's son had eaten his breakfast on the following morning, he went off to the woods once more, with his dogs and his gun, as he had done on each of the two days before. This time he went deeper than ever into the wood, and he saw three times as many birds as he had seen the previous day. He kept on shooting till he had the height of a hill of dead birds, and he ordered the strong dog, Heavy-Load, to throw them up on his back and take them home, and he did.

On their way home they had not gone far when the three dogs stopped, and they gathered together and seemed to be whispering to each other. They were not long whispering like this when the king's son saw a big giant coming towards them, and his gullet was wide open, as if to swallow them. Heavy-Load threw the birds off his back and jumped up and took a grip of the giant's throat, and the other two dogs began to tear the flesh off his bones.

The giant begged the king's son to call the dogs off before they would kill him, and he promised to give him his castle and all his riches.

"It is the finest castle in the world," said the giant. "The door-posts and the doors are made of gold and silver, and there isn't a corner in it where there isn't a heap of every kind of jewel and precious stone. And you need do nothing for me except to throw me into my own big chest and turn the key on the lid, and you need not fear any trouble or hindrance from me from that on."

So far so good. The king's son shouted at the dogs to stop attacking the giant, and he ordered the strong dog to throw him up on his back and carry him to his castle. They walked on till they came to his castle, and they threw the giant into a big chest that they found there. The king's son closed the lid on the chest and turned the key on it.

He went through the castle then, and there was not a hole or a corner in it where there wasn't a heap of gold, of silver or of precious stones. After that he made supper for himself and the three dogs. When they had eaten their supper they jumped up on the lid of the giant's chest, stretched themselves out, and went to sleep till morning. The king's son searched around till he found the giant's big bed. He got into it and slept as soundly as ever he did in his life.

So far so good. He got up early in the morning and he made breakfast for himself and his dogs. Then he thought to himself that he would go and get his sister, and that they would live in the castle. So he set out for the nobleman's house and the nobleman was outside to greet and welcome him, as usual, and was delighted to see him back safe and sound. His master then asked him what had happened that he had not come back the night before. The king's son told him that the giant of the wood had attacked him.

"Oh," said the nobleman, "that is the ugly villain that killed my seven sons."

"I'll go bail," said the king's son, "that he will never kill another person," and then he told the nobleman what he had done with the giant, and about the great riches he had found, piled up, in every corner of his castle.

"And now, " said he, "I have come to get my sister, so that we may go and live in that fine castle for a while."

"It would be better for you," said the nobleman, "to bring the riches here, for that castle is under magic, and you do not know what may happen to you there."

"I am not afraid of the magic," said the king's son. "It is the finest and most beautiful castle in the world, and I am going to live in it."

So far so good. The king's son took his sister with him to the giant's castle. She was delighted at everything she saw there, and they settled down very happily to live in it. They were not there long when, one day, the king's son told his sister that he was going out hunting, and that she was to take good care of the castle until he would come back. He got his gun then, and his three dogs, and off he went.

He was not long gone when, out through the keyhole of the chest, the giant began to talk to the young woman. He started off with a lot of flattering talk, and said he was greatly in love with her.

"Why don't you let me out of this chest," he coaxed, "and I will marry you, and we'll have the castle to ourselves."

And so it was. The girl let the giant out of the chest and they settled between them that they would kill her brother, so that the castle would be truly their own.

"Now," said the giant, "go down to the room and bring me up my Sword of Light. Hang it over the door, here, and when your brother will come, it will fall down and take the head off him."

She did as the giant bade her; she brought the Sword of Light and hung it up over the door.

The king's son had not gone far when the three dogs sat down and began whispering to one another. Then they turned around and made back home to the castle. When he saw the dogs returning, the king's son thought that the giant must have got out of the chest by magic and killed his sister. So he turned around too, and ran back to the castle as fast as his legs would carry him.

Back in the castle the giant warned the young woman to keep on the lookout all the time, for fear her brother would come back before they expected him, "For if those dogs come, they will attack me and tear me to pieces."

Very soon the girl saw her brother coming back at full speed, and the three dogs racing out in front of him. The giant had only barely time to jump into the chest and have the lid closed down on him, when they came panting in the door. Swift, the speedy dog, came in first, he came in the door of the castle in three bounds. As he came through the door of the room where the giant was in the chest, the Sword of Light fell down on him, and cut off the tip of his tail. The girl took the Sword of Light then and hid it.

Her brother came in then, and he asked her was there anything wrong in the castle. She told him that there was not anything at all wrong.

"By my word," said he, "when I saw the dogs returning, I

thought that the giant must have got out of the chest and killed you."

"Oh," said she, "don't be thinking any such thing. The ugly beast never stirred since you went out this morning."

On the following morning the king's son went off to the woods again, and took his three dogs with him. When his sister found he was gone, she raised up the lid of the chest and let the giant out.

"Now," said the giant, "the best thing for us to do is to get your brother to lock the dogs up in a room, and then we can do what we like with him."

On this day, as on the day before, the king's son had not gone far when the dogs turned back again. He followed them, as quickly as he could, as he thought there must be something wrong in the castle. As before, the young woman was keeping a lookout, and when she saw the dogs coming back, she warned the giant. He jumped back into the chest again, and she put the lock on it, before the dogs came in.

Her brother came in then, and he asked her if anything had happened while he was away, but she said that nothing at all had happened, and that she did not know in the world why the dogs came back.

"But these dogs are frightening me," she said, "coming racing in around me, like wild boars. I would be glad if you would put them in a room by themselves tonight, and lock the room, for I have no peace or ease while they are going loose through the castle."

Her brother said he would like to please her, but he would not like to lock up the dogs.

"They are my tried and trusted friends," he said, "and they are doing no harm to anyone, so I will not lock them up."

The young woman then got very cross and angry, and she began to beat the dogs down off the lid of the giant's chest, where they always liked to lie. One of the dogs turned around on her and bit her finger as she was beating him off the chest. She roared and she screamed then, and she pretended that she was very badly bitten, and she said that her brother should kill the dogs altogether, since they were so dangerous. Her brother then said that he would take the dogs with him to another part of the castle, out of her sight, but he said that he would not lock them up.

When the king's son left his sister, she began to think of a way to get rid, not only of the dogs, but of her own brother. Late in the night she came to him, and said that her hand was very sore where the dog bit her, and that nothing in the world would cure it but to rub it to the tongue of the magic bull that lived in the Eastern World. And she said that she would surely die if he did not go to the Eastern World and get the tongue of the magic bull for her. She knew that no one ever came back alive who had ever gone anywhere near that bull.

And so it was. The king's son prepared the giant's big ship for the journey; he put into it provisions for a year and a day, he raised his sails to the wind and, with his three dogs, went off to the Eastern World.

Now the daughter of the King of the Eastern World was strolling on the beach one day when she saw a beautiful ship coming in. She was greatly surprised, especially when she saw a handsome young man on board with no company with him except three dogs. He saluted her, and she welcomed him and took him to her father, the king. He told the king that he came to the Eastern World for the tongue of the magic bull.

"I'm sorry to hear that," said the king, "for no one who ever went near him has come safe from that beast. The land is a desert for seven miles all around him, for he kills any creature, big or small, that he sees."

The king's daughter began to cry then, when she heard that the king's son was bent on going against the bull. She begged him not to go, for she had given him her heart's love from the first minute she had laid eyes on him. But he told her he had pledged his word to go against the bull and to bring back his tongue to cure his sister, and that he would leave her his three dogs as company for her while he was away, and he asked her to take good care of them, "for they are my truly loyal friends."

He went off then to the south of the country on the following morning. The bull saw him in the far distance, and he let a bellow out of him that was heard in the farthest corner of the Western World. He lowered his horns then and started to race towards him to destroy him.

Now, the three dogs heard that bellow, and knowledge came to the clever one — All-Knowing — that his master was in danger from the magic bull, that no one living could kill. So the three dogs whispered together for a while, then they leaped over the wall of the castle of the King of the Eastern World, and raced as fast as they could after their master. By this time the magic bull was drawing very near him, his horns down to gore him. But the speedy dog, Swift, reached the bull before the others, and took a grip on his tail. The bull turned around to kill him, but Swift was too quick for him, and he could not catch him. So he kept the bull turning around and around like that after him till the two other dogs came up. The strong dog, Heavy-Load, jumped up on the bull then, and sunk his teeth in his nose, and kept him standing while the other two attacked him. In the end they knocked him down, and the king's son cut out his tongue and brought it back to the palace with him.

The princess was delighted when she saw him come back safely, but she was sadder than ever, on the following day, when he said he had to return to his own country. She began to cry and lament, until the king's son told her that he would come back in a year and a day and marry her.

He did not say anything that was not true. He and his three dogs went off in his ship, and they sailed and sailed until they came to the castle of the big giant. His sister greatly wondered when she saw him coming. She told him that she was on the point of death from the pain in her hand, but, of course, she was only pretending. Her brother rubbed the tongue of the magic bull to her hand, and she pretended that it cured the pain. Then she told him that the big giant was loose, as he broke the chest one day and came out, but that he had such a fear of the dogs that he ran off, and she had never seen him since. The king's son told her then about all he had seen in the Eastern World, and of the princess he was going to marry, and he said that she should come with him to the wedding. She said she would go, but that he would have to leave the three dogs behind, for she would not go into the ship with them for fear they would tear her to pieces. Since he had no choice in the matter, the king's son left the dogs after him in the castle of the giant, and he and his sister set off in the ship for the Eastern World.

The daughter of the King of the Eastern World was delighted to see the king's son back again, and they were married after a few days. His sister then went to the King of the Eastern World and asked him to allow her to dress the bridal bed for her brother and his bride, and he gave her leave to do so. She had brought the giant's Sword of Light with her, unknown to her brother, and she hung it up over the bed. When her brother got into the bed, the sword fell on him and killed him.

His sister then went to the King of the Eastern World and

told him that it was his own daughter, the princess, who had killed him with the sword. The King of the Eastern World gave judgment that the princess, his own daughter, should be burned on account of the dreadful crime of killing her own husband. But the king said that, since she was his own daughter, he would give her a respite of a year and a day before burning her.

As to the three dogs, they were very sad and sorrowful at being left behind by their master, and they barked and they whined all day and all night. After a day or two knowledge came to the clever dog, All-Knowing, that the giant was hiding in the solar, on the ground floor of the castle. The three of them went down to tear him to pieces, but they found the heavy door was locked. The strong dog, Heavy-Load, put his shoulder to it, to break it in, but if he did, the giant put his back against it, on the inside, and Heavy-Load could not budge it.

The three dogs then started to scrape the door with their nails, and to gnaw it with their teeth. It wasn't too long till they had a hole made in it. But when they rushed in through the hole, wasn't the giant walking out a door on the other side of the solar!

The giant then made off into the thick woods, as quickly as his legs would carry him. They kept going till they came to the very deepest part of the wood. There they saw the giant up on the highest tree of all that were in the wood. They looked up at the giant on the top of the tree, and he looked down at them, and he had no fear of them any longer, for he knew they could not climb up the tree after him.

So far so good. The three dogs sat down then, and they began whispering to one another. After a while Heavy-Load, the strong dog, got up and put his shoulder to the trunk of the tree, and put it swaying and swinging to and fro, till at last he knocked it with a great crash. The giant fell with the tree, and he broke his neck and died on the spot.

Now, the three dogs said they would go to the Eastern World in search of their master. But they did not know how they would cross the sea; it was too far to swim, and they had neither a boat nor a ship. The clever dog set himself to think out a plan for them, and after a while he said that he knew where there was a fisherman's boat tied up, not too far away. He said they could take that and set sail at once. They followed him then and found the boat. They cut the mooring ropes with their teeth, and All-Knowing made a rudder for them. After that they hoisted sails, and as there was nothing to stop them, they faced for the Eastern World.

When they got there they made no delay in the castle, but made quickly to their master's grave. They scratched away the earth till they came to the body. They took it up and licked every bit of it all over. Then the king's son rose up as alive and as healthy as ever he was in his life before.

He went then to the King of the Eastern World, and he told him that it was not his daughter who had killed him, but his own sister, with the giant's Sword of Light. And on the fire that they had got ready for the princess, they put the false, deceiving sister, and burned her to ashes.

The king's son said farewell to his father-in-law then, took his wife and the three dogs, and set sail for the castle of the big giant.

On their way to the ship they were met by the young woman who had given him the three dogs. She came up to him and said:

"When you left home the first time your mother died of grief, and I was a messenger she sent to you from the other world to help you in every danger. You will not be needing the dogs any

longer, as the big giant is dead, and the enchantment is taken
from the castle. The castle, and everything that is in it, is yours,
for yourself and your wife from this on."

She said goodbye to him then, and called the three dogs, and
walked away.

The king's son and his wife lived a long and happy life in the
castle, and his children, and his children's children after him.
And some of his children's children are still living there, and
there is not alive, on the face of the earth, a single one of the
posterity of the old king who gave the bad advice to his children.

The Daughter of the King of Greece

THERE WAS a king in Ireland long ago, and it is often there was, and will be again. He had three sons. The eldest one said to his father, one day, that the kingdom was too small and would not support them all, so he asked to have a cake baked for him, and he would go off and try to make a livelihood for himself. So far so good. His father called him on the following morning and he told him there were two cakes ready for him — a small cake with his blessing, and a large cake with his curse, and that he could take his choice of the two. The son said that since he was taking to the road he would need plenty of provisions, and so he would take the large cake and his curse.

He got the large cake. He rose early out of bed. He washed his hands and his face and set out. He turned to the southeast, and asked for God's guidance, and if he didn't, let it be so. He went on till night began to overtake him. He got hungry then, and he sat down on a little hummock, and, drawing out his cake, he began to eat it. He was not long there when a little robin redbreast came in front of him, and said:

"King's son from Ireland, will you give me a little scrap, or a few crumbs, or any little bit for my young ones?"

"Indeed, by my troth, I will not," said the king's son. "What I have is little enough for myself, and I not knowing what journey is in front of me."

The words were hardly out of his mouth when the ground opened under him, and he was swallowed down into it.

The king was waiting at home, day after day, for some news or tidings of his son. Not a word did he get. So when a year and a day had passed, the second son went to his father and said that he should set out and see if he could find any trace or tidings of his brother. He asked that food for the road should be got ready for him.

The father then gave the second son the choice of the two cakes, just as he had done with his eldest son. The second son too chose the large cake and the father's curse. He went on the road then and started walking, and never stopped till he came to the same little grassy mound where his brother had sat before him to eat his supper. He drew out the cake of bread and started to eat. The robin came in front of him. He gave her the same re-fusal, and the same thing happened to him as had happened to his brother — the ground opened underneath him and swal-lowed him up.

So that was the way things were till another year and a day had passed. The third son then went to his father and said that it was two years since his oldest brother had left home, and that it was a year and a day since his second brother had gone, and that he could not get any peace or ease till he would find out what had happened to them. He asked to have a cake baked for him, and he said that he himself would set out tomorrow and see if he could find any news of them.

And so it was. The king had two cakes made for him — a small cake with his blessing, and a big cake with his curse, and he called his son and he gave him the choice of the two cakes. He took the small cake with his father's blessing and set off.

THE DAUGHTER OF THE KING OF GREECE

He followed the same path that his two brothers before him had taken, and he kept on going till the evening was drawing in. He got hungry, and he sat down on the same little mound where each of his two brothers had sat, and he drew out his cake and began to eat. The little robin came in front of him, and said:

"King's son from Ireland, will you give me a crumb, or a scrap, or some little bit for my little ones?"

"Indeed then, I will give you as much as you want, more than you will be able to take away with you. Come here, and take as much as you can carry."

"O, king's son from Ireland," said the little robin, "I know where you are going, and if your brothers had said the same thing to me, they would not be in the plight they are in today. They were swallowed into the ground here, and you need not try to find any more tidings of them. King's son from Ireland, where are you going to spend the night?"

"I don't know in the world," said the king's son. "I have no place in my mind at all where I may seek shelter."

"I will tell you," said the robin, "where you will go. There is an old druid living down there, at the corner of the wood; let you go down to him, and he will give you shelter for the night. After your supper he will ask you where you are bound for. Say to him that you do not know, and that came to him looking for advice."

The king's son thanked the little robin a thousand times, and he made straight down for the house of the old druid. He went in. The old druid gave a hundred thousand welcomes to him, the King of Ireland's son, and he told him he could have his choice of anything that was in his poor house that night.

As time went on, after supper, just as the robin had told him, the old druid asked him for what corner of the walls of the world he was making.

"I don't know at all for what place I'd best make," said the king's son, "so I came here to ask your advice."

"Are you a good warrior?" asked the old druid.

"I never got much chance yet to show my strength," said the king's son. "But I think I would do as well as the next in a combat."

"Good enough," said the druid. "Rise early in the morning. There is a pond under a tree, down there below. Let you go and hide yourself in the tree. The daughter of the King of Greece will come there tomorrow with her twelve ladies-in-waiting. They will go swimming in the pool, and they will leave their clothes on the bank. Let you take the clothes and climb up the tree with them. They will call out to you and beg you to leave their clothes behind you. Let you say that you won't. Then they will say to you that they will give you anything you ask if you but give them their clothes. Then say that it isn't much you are going to ask of them, and that all you are going to ask is to be given the little lame duck that is swimming in the pond behind them. They will say then that the little lame duck is no use to you, and that they will give you anything else you ask. Tell them then, that you will neither ask for nor take any other thing but the little lame duck. You will get her in the heel of the hunt, and when you do, take her advice, and do everything she will tell you. And now, that's all the advice I have to give you."

The king's son did everything he was told by the druid, and he got the little lame duck in exchange for the maidens' clothes. He took her with him then, and it was not long till she turned into the most beautiful young woman on whom the sun ever shone. He fell in love with her straightaway, and she fell in love with him.

She told him that she herself was the daughter of the King of

Greece, and that her stepsister, the one he saw yesterday, had turned her into a duck by magic in order to set her aside and put her out of the way. She said that her father, the King of Greece, was against her as well. Then she asked him if he were a good warrior, "for, if ever you want to make me your wife, you will have to fight bravely and valiantly for me before you can break the magic spells they have woven around me," she told him.

"I never got much chance yet to prove my fighting skill," said he, "but I pledge myself now to do my best to free you from their spells."

"Well," said she, "my father needs a cowherd. Go off to him now, and tell him that you are a cowherd looking for hire. He will settle with you, as he badly needs a herd. Don't take any wages from him, but ask him for permission to sleep in the Room of the Wind. It will be hard for you to get him to agree to that, for it is seven years since I was put under magic and driven out of the window of that room, the northeast window of the courtyard, and the room has never been unlocked since. He will agree to your bargain in the end, and then he will ask you to eat your supper with him. Tell him then that you have no mind for food at all, that you ate a lot of wild fruit in the woods, and that it is more sleep than hunger that is preying on you. Then ask him to give you the key to the Room of the Wind so that you may go to sleep. You will get the key then. Go to the room, unlock the door, and I will be inside before you."

And that is how it was. Everything happened just as she said it would. When he opened the door, there she was, inside before him, with a fine, bright fire burning on the hearth, without smoke, without blackness and without a wavering or a faltering in its blazing. The room was decked out with vessels of gold and silver, and there was a choice and a selection of every kind of food and drink that was to be had at that time.

They made three parts of the night then, a time for eating and drinking, a time for playing music, and a time for telling stories. Then, in the twinkling of an eye, she left him, and he spent the rest of the night in a deep, calm slumber till morning.

He rose early, and she had the first meal of the day ready for him, and when he had eaten, she asked him was he ready to go out herding the cows. He said he was, and more than ready.

"You have a hard fight in front of you today," she told him. "As soon as you let out the cows they will all go in one rush, over into the land of the giants that is bordering on my father's land. They won't be there long when the giant of the three heads, the three humps and the three necks will come to attack you. He will be in a towering rage. He will ask you with what kind of weapons you wish to fight, or what kind of combat you want to choose. Tell him that you want the tough, ferocious wrestling match. While he is wrestling with you the only word he will say is that it is no wonder that you wrestle so strong and fiercely, considering the beautiful woman to whom you are betrothed. Let you say to him then, that his own mother is more beautiful than she. If you give him any other answer he will gain the upper hand of you, and he will take the head off you on the spot."

The king's son then went and let out the cows, and he walked after them quietly. They walked away before him, and they never stopped until they came to the giants' lands. They were not long there till he heard the noise of the branches being torn, and twisted, and snapped apart, and of the old brushwood being broken and rended. It was the giant of the three heads, the three humps and the three necks tearing all before him as he came through the wood.

"Fi, fo, fum, I smell the blood of an Irishman on a land that is not his own! And if right is not wrong he will pay for it with his head," said the giant.

"Confound you, ugly giant!" said the king's son. "I didn't come here to give you any satisfaction, but to take good, hard satisfaction out of your bones and out of your flesh."

"Good enough, king's son," said the giant. "What way will you fight? Do you prefer a fierce, hard wrestling match, or a bout of hard swordplay — our blades going in and out between each other's ribs?"

"I choose a fierce, hard bout of wrestling, for that is what I practiced with my noble comrades at my father's court."

They made for each other then, as would two stalwart fighting men, or two mountain bulls. They made soft places hard, and hard places soft. They drew springs of clear well water through hard rock. And at the end of every hour the giant would say that it was a small wonder that the king's son should make such a strong stand, considering the beautiful woman to whom he was betrothed. The king's son would always answer that the giant's own mother was more beautiful than she. But as the fight went on, the king's son was not gaining, so the little robin came before him and said:

"Oh, king's son from Ireland, you are far from your keening women now, your corpse-washers and your nursing women, but if you were to put forth all your strength, and give one good twist to that ugly, ungainly fellow, you would have the upper hand of him in a short while."

When he heard these words from the robin, the king's son put forth all his strength and power, and he made for the giant, and he gave him such a twist that he got him down on his knees; with the second twist he got him down on his hips; and with the third, he put him on his back.

"Your heads to me, giant," he said.

"Don't take my heads," said the giant, "and I will give you half my kingdom to the day of my death, and my whole kingdom from that day on, and as well I'll give you my little magic wand."

"Where is that?" asked the king's son.

"It is over on top of that rock yonder."

"I will have those and your heads too," said the king's son, drawing his sword and taking the three heads off the giant. He cut a withe in the woods, and he drew it through their cheeks and threw them over his shoulder. He went to collect his cows then, and drove them home.

By this time the King of Greece thought that the herd should be coming back with the cows, and he sent the servant girl out to see if he were coming. The servant girl came in and said that she could not see a bit of him nor of the cows.

"He isn't coming, and you won't see him," said the king.

After another while he told her to go out again and see if the herd were coming yet. This time she wasn't long outside when she ran in and said:

"Here he is, master! He is coming now, and he has the three heads of the giant on his shoulder."

The king jumped up, and he took three steps out the door of the courtyard to meet the herd. He put his two arms around his neck, and he nearly smothered him with kisses, and drowned him with tears, and he dried him with kerchiefs of silk and satin. He told him then to go inside and eat his supper. And he said that in all the time that he himself was there, no herd had ever come home alive till now.

"Oh, I am not hungry at all," said the king's son from Ireland, "there was a lot of wild fruit in the woods and I ate my fill of them. It is more weary I am than hungry, so if you will give me the key I will go to sleep."

He got the key and he opened the door, and the beautiful maiden was inside before him again, with a fine, steadily blazing fire burning on the hearth. She went towards him, and she put healing balm on his wounds, and he was then as well and as healthy as he was when he was leaving the house in the morning. Then they passed the night as merrily and as pleasantly as before. The king's son got up early next morning, and when he was ready to go out to do his day's work, the daughter of the King of Greece said to him:

"There is no doubt at all that you made a good fight yesterday, but yesterday's fight was not the same thing at all as the one you will have to endure today, and for fear anything may part us from one another, I will give you this ring to keep safely till you see me again. The giant you wrestled with yesterday was younger than the one you will have to face today. He will utter no word to you all during the struggle, except that it is small wonder that you are wrestling so bravely, seeing the beauty of the maiden to whom you are betrothed. If you give him any other answer, except that his own mother is more beautiful than she, he will have the head off you in no time at all."

"Do not be afraid, I will not forget your advice," he said.

He went off then after the cows, and they never stopped or delayed till they came to the territory of the giants. The king's son was not long there till he heard the cracking and the tearing of branches coming towards him. The giant of today was making twice as much noise coming through the wood as did the giant of the previous day. He made straight for the king's son.

"Blood and hatred on you; you killed my young brother yesterday, who was only a miserable three hundred years old. It was only because we were short of timber that we took him out of the cradle so soon, but I will take sore satisfaction out of you today for having killed him."

They faced each other then, and fierce and hard as was the struggle the previous day, this day's struggle was harder and fiercer still. Towards evening the giant was gaining the upper hand, and the little robin came, and said to the king's son to put forth all his strength or he would be beaten in the contest. The king's son then made his greatest effort, and he conquered the giant. Then he cut off his heads and he took them home with him to the King of Greece. The king came six steps out through the door of the court to meet and to welcome him, and he asked him once again to take his supper along with him. But the king's son refused all food, and he gave the same excuse as he gave the night before. He asked the King of Greece then for the key to the Room of the Wind, he unlocked the door, went in and found the maiden inside before him. She cured all his wounds with healing balm, as she had done on the night before, and then they spent the night, or a portion of it, in merrymaking.

On the following morning, when he was ready to go, she said to him that the combats he had on the two previous days were nothing to the one he would have today. And she told him not to forget her advice — that every time the giant would say that it was no wonder he was fighting so well, since he was be-trothed to such a beautiful maiden, he was to say that the giant's own mother was more beautiful still. "Be sure," she warned him, "and follow my advice."

He went out after the cows then. The giant of the nine heads, the nine humps and the nine necks came and attacked him. They fought bravely till evening, till the robin came and urged on the king's son to put forth his greatest strength. Then, to make a long story short, he conquered the giant and took the nine heads off him. He took the heads back then to the King of Greece, who had come nine steps outside the door of the court to meet him. And however great the welcome he had for him on the other two nights, his welcome on this night was twice as great. He began then to urge the king's son from Ireland to eat his supper along with him, but the king's son gave the same excuse as he had given before. Then he asked for the key, and he went to the Room of the Wind. He took the lock off the door and went in. The maiden was inside before him, and she treated his wounds with healing balm, as she had done each night.

She called him early on the following morning, and she said to him: "There is no doubt that you have proved yourself a brave warrior on each of the last three days, but the contests with the giants were as nothing compared with the fight that is before you today. The Wild Hag herself, the mother of the giants, will be facing you today. She has spent seven years in a forge, putting a sharp, hard edge on her fingernails. There is no scratch that she will give you that she will not take much flesh and blood off you with her nails. And every minute she will say to you that it is no wonder you are making a strong fight, since you are betrothed to such a beautiful maiden. Say to her every time that she herself is more beautiful, for if you admit anything else, she will get the upper hand of you and kill you on the spot."

"I will remember your advice," said he, and away with him, after his cows, to the land of the giants. They had scarcely crossed over the boundary when he heard a thunderous noise, so loud it was that he thought the earth was shaking under him. Just then he saw the Wild Hag coming towards him. The farthest back teeth in her head she was using as crutches to swing herself along, and she had seven acres of beard dragging after her, and it plowed and harrowed the ground as she came.

"Blood and hatred on you, king's son from Ireland!" she

shouted at him as she drew near. "You invaded this land, and you killed my three little children these last three days. And only for the scarcity of timber, the eldest one would be in a cradle yet, for he's only a paltry nine hundred years old. But I will have satisfaction from you today for the end you gave them."

"Confound you, you old hag," said the king's son. "It was not to give you satisfaction for them I came here, but to get hard satisfaction from your skin and your bones."

She gave a diabolical snarl then, and asked him: "Which do you want — a fierce, hard bout of wrestling, or a contest of sharp swords, playing in and out between the ribs?"

"I choose a bout of hard, fierce wrestling," said the king's son.

"That's something I will not give you," she said, leaping up in the air over his head, and only that he threw himself under the belly of a milch cow, she would have torn all the flesh off him with her long talons. He got up then and tried to defend himself from her. Every minute she would say that it was little wonder he was putting up such a hard fight, when the maiden to whom he was betrothed was so beautiful. And he would always answer that she, herself, was more beautiful. At long last she annoyed him so much that he lost his patience, his noble blood rose to his head, and he said:

"Famine take you, ugly hag! She is more beautiful than you!"

The words were hardly out of his mouth when she took a leap up in the air over him again and she tore half the flesh off him. With a second leap her talons went so deep into him that she almost laid bare his bones altogether.

Then the little robin redbreast came and spoke to him: "Alas, king's son from Ireland, you are cut to pieces by that hag's talons. But listen to me now and take my advice. She has seven magic glass mantles around her, and if you could get a good kick at her, so as to break them, she would then have the strength of only one woman."

The king's son made a kick at the hag, and he broke one of the glass mantles. A second kick broke another, and he went on till he broke the whole seven of them. She fell down in a heap then, and it was true for the robin, she now had only the strength of any one woman.

"Your head to me, hag," said the king's son.

"Oh, don't take my head, king's son, and I will give you half my kingdom to the day of my death, and the whole of it from my death on, my slender black steed, and my magic wand that is in the rock over there."

"I will have all these and your head along with them, hag!" he said, taking the head off her.

He drew a withe through the cheeks, threw the head over his shoulder, and went home driving his cows before him. When he reached the courtyard the king was a good way out in front of the door to welcome him. He was so pleased to be finished forever with the giants and with their mother, the Wild Hag, that his joy knew no bounds. He took the king's son into a fine, whitewashed courtyard with him and into a castle where there was no under-rafter to be seen inside, nor no over-rafter to be seen outside, but one single rafter binding and securing all of them together. They went through a doorway that had a lintel of sharp razors, and a threshold of hard needles, and the floor under it was sown with sharp pins and was constantly turning around.

He put his two arms around the neck of the king's son, and said that now he should have no reason to leave without having a feast with him tonight.

"I have no mind at all to eat a thing," said the king's son.

"I picked and ate a lot of fruit in the woods since morning, and it is more weariness I feel than hunger, so I will go to the Room of the Wind and go to sleep."

The King of Greece then gave him the key, and he went up to the Room of the Wind. He took the lock off the door, but he found nothing there before him but the four bare, cold walls, with no food nor no fire. He knew then that he had made a blunder, and that the beautiful maiden had gone away from him because he had admitted to the hag that she was more beautiful than she.

He stayed there till morning, shaking with cold, and his wounds opened and bled. No bit of the day stole on him. The morning, it seemed to him, was a long time coming. He thought it long till he could leave the room and go and warm himself at a fire.

The king came then and asked him what had happened, and where was his company from him last night, and was there no one to put healing balm on his wounds. He got a leech for him then and had his wounds cured. After some time the king's son from Ireland was as well as ever he was, so he went to the King of Greece to say goodbye to him.

"Wait a minute," said the King of Greece, "you can't go like that without a reward." So he went off and brought one of his daughters to him. He asked him if he had ever seen a maiden as beautiful as she was. The king's son said that he had not. The King of Greece asked him again if he had ever seen a maiden as beautiful as she, and again the king's son said he hadn't. A third time the King of Greece asked the king's son from Ireland if he had ever seen a maiden as beautiful as his daughter. This time the king's son from Ireland said:

"Leave me alone, I saw a woman whose little toe was more beautiful than her face and brow."

"There is a penalty for admitting that," said the King of
Greece. "You will not leave this place until you let me see this
beautiful maiden."

He took the king's son from Ireland then, and he put him
into a tower, and he sent a proclamation out through his kingdom that he had such a one imprisoned, and that he would behead him on such a day, at such an hour, unless the woman
would be found who was more beautiful than the king's own
daughter.

The day for the beheading came, and a great crowd gathered
as the hour appointed for the execution drew near. Then the
son of the King of Ireland was taken out to have his head cut
off. He was asked if he had anything to say before they put him
to death. He asked the King of Greece then if he would grant
him a respite for half an hour. The half hour passed and no
help came to him. He asked then for a quarter of an hour. At
the end of that time the sky darkened all around, and three
crows appeared up in the air over the heads of the crowd. The
crows flew around in a circle once, and then they came down
and landed on the ground in the middle of the crowd. They
turned into three women the minute they touched the ground.
One of them then whipped the stocking off her foot, and light
flooded out from it.

"There she is for you," said the king's son from Ireland,
"the woman more beautiful than your daughter, and her small
toe is more beautiful than your daughter's face."

Just then the three women turned into crows once more,
and rose up into the sky, and left everyone looking up after
them. The king's son from Ireland was freed, and he went away
without a word or a blessing to the King of Greece. He kept on
walking until the mist and the dew of the night were gathering

around him, and until the moon was going under the shadow of the dock leaf, and the dock leaf was fleeing before her. Cross, snappish dogs were barking in the accustomed places, and in the unwonted places there wasn't a whisper out of them. Just before the coming of darkness he saw a slender thread of smoke rising up out of a glen. He made towards it, and he saw a small house with a thatched roof. He went in. There was no one inside before him, but the half-blind, red-headed wizard who had one leg free and one leg bound.

"Good morrow to you, king's son from Ireland," said he. "It is well you came to turn the goats in for me."

"I'll turn them in for you, and welcome," said the king's son.

"Indeed, king's son, if you will bind up my other leg, I'll turn them in myself."

He tied up the wizard's leg. Out with the wizard then, and it seemed that there wasn't a goat for twenty miles around that he didn't collect and drive in. They milked them then. They drank a mug of the milk hot and a mug cold. They killed them, and they drew them through the fire and through the mire, and through long cold teeth, and they ate them. Then they sat down, one at each side of the fire, and the wizard asked the king's son if he had any news.

"I have not a bit," said the king's son. "Would you have any news yourself?"

"Blow me, if I have," said the wizard, "except that the daughter of the King of Greece was here with me last night, herself and her twelve waiting women, and not one of them could keep her from weeping her eyes out all the night, crying and lamenting without ceasing for some warrior who was fighting for her."

"Where did she go from you, wizard?" asked the king's son.

"She will be in the house of a brother of mine tonight," said the wizard.

"Where is that house, wizard?" asked the king's son.

" 'Tis a good long day's journey on that little road to south-east."

The king's son did not speak another word. They went to bed then, and it is no cause for wonder that deep, calm sleep had not come to him by the time the day brightened. He rose early. He washed his hands and his face. He turned to the southeast, and he asked God to guide him, and if he didn't, let us leave it so.

On the road a blade of grass did not grow under his feet till he reached the house of the second wizard that evening. He spent the night with him, just as he had spent the night before, and he got the same tidings of the daughter of the King of Greece — that she had gone to the house of another brother, that was a long day's journey off.

On the following morning, as soon as the sun had risen, he took to the road again, and he did not stop nor stay till he reached the house of the third wizard. The wizard gave a great welcome to the king's son, and he said it was as well he had come, as he could turn in the goats for him, just as the other two had said.

"I'll turn them in for you, and welcome," said the king's son.

"Never mind," said the wizard, "but if you would be so good as to tie up my other leg, I'll turn them in myself."

He tied up the wizard's leg, just as he had done for his two brothers. Then the wizard went out. And you would think that there wasn't a goat in Ireland that he hadn't turned in within half an hour. They milked the goats, and they drank a mug of the milk cold and a mug of it hot. They killed them then, and they drew them through the fire and through the mire, and through the long, cold teeth, and they ate them. They sat down at either side of the fire, and the wizard asked the king's son if he had any news.

"Not a bit in the world," said the king's son. "Would you have any news yourself?"

"Not a word," said the wizard, "but that the daughter of the King of Greece with her twelve waiting women were here with me last night."

"Where is she tonight, wizard?" asked the king's son.

The wizard said that she was getting married tonight in the house of her father's brother, a piece up the road outside, and that there was to be a great wedding feast, with all the warriors and champions of the whole world gathered there.

"Wizard," said the king's son, "will you come to the wedding with me?"

"Indeed, I will not," said the wizard, "for if the king saw me, he would take the head off me."

"Come on," said the king's son. "You can wait outside and I will go in, and I'll bring you out your fill of eating and drinking."

They went off then, and they never stopped going till they came to the court of the brother of the King of Greece.

"You wait here now," said the king's son to the wizard, "until I will come out."

He made off then, and went in the kitchen door. He went up to the fire, buck-leaping and capering as if he were a fool. Just at that moment the cook was going out of the kitchen carrying a big platter of meat for the wedding feast. The king's son snapped the dish of meat away from her and made out the door with it to the wizard. He threw the platter of meat down before him, and he told him to be eating that much till he came out again.

He went in again, and did the same trick. He whipped the second dish away with him also, ran out, and left that with the wizard. He went back into the kitchen again, but no sooner did he do so, than a servant man caught him, and tried to put him out, but if there were all that was in the house of servants helping him, they could not take a stir out of him.

News went up to the wedding feast then that there was some kind of a fool in the kitchen, doing damage and making off with the guests' meat. The chief steward came down and told him to be off with himself. The king's son made answer that he had no idea of going until he would see the young maiden who was to be married. The wedding party were then consulted, and they agreed to let the fool come up. Up he went, and began bounding and capering around the room, and everyone looking at his antics thought that he was a real fool. When they were tired of his tricks they brought him to the young maiden. He said he wanted to get a drink from her hand, and that he wouldn't go till he got it. She handed him a drink then. He drank it down and said that she should have a drink from him. They gave him a drink to give her. He slipped the ring that he had got from her in the Room of the Wind into the glass. She raised the glass to her head and she saw the ring at the bottom of it. She knew then that it was the king's son that was in front of her.

The priest was called in then, and she and the king's son from Ireland were married, and they had a wedding feast that lasted seven days and seven nights.

On the morning of the eighth day he asked his wife to come out boating on the sea with him. He took her out in a beautiful coracle. They hadn't gone far when the wizard came up in his own coracle.

"Oh, king's son from Ireland," said he, "let us have a race in our coracles."

"I don't mind if I do," said the king's son.

They started to race then, one against the other, and in no time at all the wizard's coracle was well out of sight in front of them. The wizard waited till they caught up with him, and said:

"King's son, I have beaten you in the race."

The king's son answered: "I was carrying more weight than you were, and only for that, you would never have beaten me."

"Very well," said the wizard, "give me the woman, and we'll have another race."

"Do not have any more to do with the wizard," said his wife, "for if you do, any hardship or agony you have suffered up to this will be nothing to what you will suffer now if you put me into the coracle with the wizard."

"Don't be afraid," said the king's son. "I'll beat him easily now, when your weight will be taken from me."

"You will not win," said she, and she did her best to prevail on him not to put her into the wizard's coracle.

But there was no persuading him. The king's son would not believe that he could not win, and he persuaded her to go into the wizard's coracle.

Off with them then, both rowing at their best, and before long there was not a bit of the wizard or his coracle to be seen. The king's son could not tell whether he had gone east or west, north or south, or whether the sea had opened and swallowed him. At last it dawned on him what the wizard was up to, and what a trick he had played on him, so he made up his mind that it was no use for him to be looking for him any longer, or to be trying to chase him. He turned his coracle around, came back into the harbor as quickly as he could and jumped out on the beach.

The king's son was sorely troubled, because he had no knowledge of where, or in what place in the wide world his wife was now. He could not return to her father's court, for if the king caught him, he would take the head off him. He did not know what in the world to do to find her, but he faced southeast, and he asked God to put him on the right road, and if he didn't, let it be so.

He walked on then till evening was catching up on him, and at the coming of dark he saw a king's court, and he went in there. Who should be inside before him but his wife! He made over to her, and started to hug and kiss her with joy at finding her again. But she told him that it was no good for him to be kissing her, as he could never get her back again.

He asked her then why this was, and who was to keep her from him. She told him that this was the wizard's house, and that the sooner he would go the better, for if the wizard came back he would kill both of them.

"I will never go from here without taking you with me," said he, "and I will gamble my life on that."

"It is hard to kill the wizard," she said, "for he has two lives. When he is leaving home he puts one of them for safekeeping into a hen's egg that is in the middle of that tree, growing out there, opposite the door. Now," said she, "there is an old rusty axe upstairs, under a bed, and that is the only axe that will cut down that tree. But you must fell it with one blow, for when the tree is struck, it will let a shout out of it, and the wizard will hear that, no matter in what part of the world he is. At present he is in the Eastern World. When he hears that shout he will be back and standing in front of you in the twinkling of an eye, and he will try to kill you. Then, unless you have the egg ready to throw at him, and to hit him with it in a certain spot under his left breast, he will make an end of you. If you manage to hit him with the egg, in the right spot, he will fall down dead, in a heap of jelly, and we will be free."

"I will try my best," said the king's son, running up the stairs for the axe. He went over to the tree then, and he struck it a strong blow, and no sooner did he hit it than a loud wailing scream came out of the tree, and it fell to the ground. The king's son then took a hold of the egg that was inside in the middle of it, and he had hardly got it in his hand than the wizard was behind him, and making an attempt to kill him with his drawn sword. But the king's son was equal to him, for before the wizard had time to aim a blow at him, he hit him with the egg in the spot right under his left breast, and the wizard fell dead in a heap.

His wife then ran to the king's son, and it was small wonder that she nearly smothered him with kisses, and drowned him with tears, and that she dried him with mantles of silk and satin. They made little delay after that, but got ready for the road.

They collected all the wealth of the wizard, silver, gold and jewels, and all the valuable things he had gathered from all parts of the world, and they set out for Ireland and the kingdom of his father.

They got a great welcome there, and they were given a wedding feast that lasted seven days and seven nights. After that they lived happily in Ireland, and their children after them for many a long year.

A Legend of Knockmany

*I*T SO HAPPENED that Finn and his gigantic relatives were all working at the Giant's Causeway in order to make a bridge, or, what was still better, a good stout pad-road across to Scotland, when Finn, who was very fond of his wife, Oonagh, took it into his head that he would go home and see how the poor woman got on in his absence. So accordingly he pulled up a fir tree, and after lopping off the roots and branches, made a walking stick of it and set out on his way to Oonagh.

Finn lived at this time on Knockmany Hill, which faces Culla-more, that rises up, half hill, half mountain, on the opposite side.

The truth is that honest Finn's affection for his wife was by no manner of means the whole cause of his journey home. There was at that time another giant, named Far Rua — some say he was Irish and some say he was Scotch — but whether Scotch or Irish, sorrow doubt of it but he was a *targer* (powerful fighter). No other giant of the day could stand before him; and such was his strength that, when well vexed, he could give a stamp that shook the country about him. The fame and name of him went far and near, and nothing in the shape of a man, it was said, had any chance with him in a fight. Whether the story is true or not I cannot say, but the report went that by one blow of his fist he flattened a thunderbolt, and kept it in his pocket in the shape of a pancake to show to all his enemies when they were about to fight him. Undoubtedly he had given every giant in Ireland a considerable beating, barring Finn Mac Cool himself; and he swore that he would never rest night or day, winter or summer, till he could serve Finn with the same sauce, if he could catch him. Finn, however, had a strong disinclination to meet a giant who could make a young earthquake or flatten a thunderbolt when he was angry, so accordingly he kept dodging about from place to place — not much to his credit as a Trojan, to be sure — whenever he happened to get the hard word that Far Rua was on the scent of him. And the long and the short of it was that he heard Far Rua was coming to the Causeway to have a trial of strength with him; and he was, naturally enough, seized in consequence with a very warm and sudden fit of affection for his wife, who was delicate in her health, poor woman, and leading, besides, a very lonely, uncomfortable life of it in his absence.

"God save all here," said Finn good-humoredly, putting his honest face into his own door.

"Musha, Finn, avick, an' you're welcome to your own Oonagh, you darlin' bully." Here followed a smack that is said to have made the waters of the lake curl, as it were, with kindness and sympathy.

"Faith," said Finn, "beautiful; and how are you, Oonagh — and how did you sport your figure during my absence, my bilberry?"

"Never a merrier — as bouncing a grass widow as ever there was in sweet 'Tyrone among the bushes.'"

Finn gave a short, good-humored cough, and laughed most heartily to show how much he was delighted that she made herself happy in his absence.

"An' what brought you home so soon, Finn?" said she.

"Why, avourneen," said Finn, putting in his answer in the proper way, "never the thing but the purest of love and affection for yourself. Sure, you know that's truth, anyhow, Oonagh."

Finn spent two or three happy days with Oonagh, and felt himself very comfortable considering the dread he had of Far Rua. This, however, grew upon him so much that his wife could not but perceive something lay on his mind which he kept altogether to himself. Let a woman alone in the meantime for ferreting or wheedling a secret out of her good man when she wishes. Finn was a proof of this.

"It's this Far Rua," said he, "that's troublin' me. When the fellow gets angry and begins to stamp he'll shake you a whole townland, and it's well known that he can stop a thunderbolt, for he always carries one with him in the shape of a pancake to show to anyone that might misdoubt it."

As he spoke he clapped his thumb in his mouth, as he always did when he wanted to prophesy or to know anything.

"He's coming," said Finn; "I see him below at Dungannon."

"An' who is it, avick?"

"Far Rua," replied Finn, "and how to manage I don't know. If I run away I am disgraced, and I know that sooner or later I must meet him, for my thumb tells me so."

"When will he be here?" says she.

"Tomorrow, about two o'clock," replied Finn with a groan.

"Don't be cast down," said Oonagh; "depend on me, and, maybe, I'll bring you out of this scrape better than ever you could bring yourself."

This quieted Finn's heart very much, for he knew that Oonagh was hand-and-glove with the fairies; and indeed, to tell the truth, she was supposed to be a fairy herself. If she was, however, she must have been a kind-hearted one, for by all accounts she never did anything but good in the neighborhood.

Now, it so happened that Oonagh had a sister named Granua living opposite to them, on the very top of Cullamore, which I have mentioned already, and this Granua was quite as powerful as herself. The beautiful valley that lies between the Gran-lisses is not more than three or four miles broad, so that of a summer evening Granua and Oonagh were able to hold many an agreeable conversation across it, from one hilltop to the other. Upon this occasion Oonagh resolved to consult her sister as to what was best to be done in the difficulty that surrounded them.

"Granua," said she, "are you at home?"

"No," said the other, "I'm picking bilberries at Althadha-wan [the Devil's Glen]."

"Well," said Oonagh, "go up to the top of Cullamore, look about you, and then tell us what you see."

"Very well," replied Granua. After a few minutes: "I am there now."

"What do you see?" asked the other.

"Goodness be about us!" exclaimed Granua. "I see the biggest giant that ever was known coming up from Dungan-non."

"Ay," said Oonagh, "there's our difficulty. That's Far Rua, and he's comin' up now to leather Finn. What's to be done?"

"I'll call to him," she replied, "to come up to Cullamore and refresh himself, and maybe that will give you and Finn time to think of some plan to get yourselves out of the scrape. But," she proceeded, "I'm short of butter, having in the house only half a dozen firkins, and as I'm to have a few giants and giant-esses to spend the evenin' with me I'd feel thankful, Oonagh, if you'd throw me up fifteen or sixteen tubs, or the largest *miscaun** you've got, and you'll oblige me very much."

"I'll do that with a heart and a half," replied Oonagh; "and, indeed, Granua, I feel myself under great obligations to you for your kindness in keeping him off us till we see what can be done; for what would become of us all if anything happened to Finn, poor man!"

She accordingly got the largest *miscaun* of butter she had — which might be about the weight of a couple of dozen mill-stones, so that you can easily judge of its size — and calling up her sister: "Granua," says she, "are you ready? I'm going to throw you up a *miscaun,* so be prepared to catch it."

"I will," said the other. "A good throw, now, and take care it does not fall short."

Oonagh threw it, but in consequence of her anxiety about Finn and Far Rua she forgot to say the charm that was to send it up, so that instead of reaching Cullamore, as she expected, it fell about halfway between the two hills at the edge of the Broad Bog, near Augher.

"My curse upon you!" she exclaimed. "You've disgraced me. I now change you into a gray stone. Lie there as a testimony of what has happened, and may evil betide the first living man that will ever attempt to move or injure you!"

And, sure enough, there it lies to this day, with the mark of the four fingers and thumb imprinted on it, exactly as it came out of her hand.

"Never mind," said Granua, "I must only do the best I can with Far Rua. If all fail, I'll give him a *cast* [measure] of heather broth, or a panada of oak bark. But, above all things, think of some plan to get Finn out of the scrape he's in, or

* *miscaun:* a ball of butter.

he's a lost man. You know you used to be sharp and ready-witted; and my own opinion is, Oonagh, that it will go hard with you, or you'll outdo Far Rua yet."

She then made a high smoke on the top of the hill, after which she put her finger in her mouth and gave three whistles, and by that Far Rua knew that he was invited to the top of Cullamore — for this was the way that the Irish long ago gave a sign to all strangers and travelers to let them know they were welcome to come and take share of whatever was going.

In the meantime Finn was very melancholy, and did not know what to do, or how to act at all. Far Rua was an ugly customer, no doubt, to meet with; and, moreover, the idea of the confounded "cake" aforesaid flattened the very heart within him. What chance could he have, strong and brave as he was, with a man who could, when put in a passion, walk the country into earthquakes and knock thunderbolts into pancakes? The thing was impossible, and Finn knew not on what hand to turn him. Right or left, backward or forward, where to go he could form no guess whatever.

"Oonagh," said he, "can you do anything for me? Where's all your invention? Am I to be skivered like a rabbit before your eyes and to have my name disgraced forever in the sight of all my tribe, and me the best man among them? How am I to fight this man-mountain — this huge cross between an earthquake and a thunderbolt — with a pancake in his pocket that was once . . . ?"

"Be aisy, Finn," replied Oonagh. "Troth, I'm ashamed of you. Keep your toe in your pump, will you? Talking of pancakes, maybe we'll give him as good as any he brings with him — thunderbolts or otherwise. If I don't treat him to as smart feeding as he's got this many a day, don't trust Oonagh again. Leave him to me, and do just as I bid you."

This relieved Finn very much, for, after all, he had great
confidence in his wife, knowing, as he did, that she had got him
out of many a quandary before. The present, however, was the
greatest of all; but still, he began to get courage and to eat his
victuals as usual. Oonagh then drew the nine woolen threads of
different colors, which she always did to find out the best way of
succeeding in anything of importance she went about. She
then plaited them into three plaits, with three colors in each,
putting one on her right arm, one round her heart, and the
third round her right ankle, for then she knew that nothing
could fail her that she undertook.

Having everything now prepared, she sent round to the
neighbors and borrowed one and twenty iron griddles, which
she took and kneaded into the hearts of one and twenty cakes of
bread, and these she baked on the fire in the usual way, setting
them aside in the cupboard according as they were done. She
then put down a large pot of new milk, which she made into
curds and whey, and gave Finn the instructions how to use
the curds when Far Rua should come. Having done all this, she
sat down quite contented waiting for his arrival on the next
day about two o'clock, that being the hour at which he was
expected — for Finn knew as much by the sucking of his
thumb. Now, this was a curious property that Finn's thumb
had; but notwithstanding all the wisdom and logic he used to
suck out of it, it could never have stood to him here were it
not for the wit of his wife. In this very thing, moreover, he was
very much resembled by his great foe, Far Rua; for it was well
known that the huge strength that he possessed all lay in the
middle finger of his right hand, and that if he happened by any
chance to lose it, he was no more, notwithstanding his bulk, than
a common man.

At length the next day he was seen coming across the

valley, and Oonagh knew that it was time to commence opera-
tions. She immediately made the cradle, and desired Finn to
lie down in it and cover himself up with the clothes.

"You must pass for your own child," said she, "so just lie
there snug and say nothing, but be guided by me."

This, to be sure, was wormwood to Finn — I mean going into
the cradle in such a cowardly manner — but he knew Oonagh
very well; and finding that he had nothing else for it, with a
very rueful face he gathered himself into it and lay snug,
as she had desired him.

About two o'clock, as he had been expected, Far Rua
came in.

"God save all here!" said he. "Is this where the great Finn
Mac Cool lives?"

"Indeed it is, honest man," replied Oonagh. "God save you
kindly — won't you be sitting?"

"Thank you, ma'am," says he, sitting down. "You're Mrs.
Mac Cool, I suppose?"

"I am," says she, "and I have no reason, I hope, to be
ashamed of my husband."

"No," said the other, "he has the name of being the strongest
and bravest man in Ireland. But, for all that, there's a man not
far from you that's very anxious of taking a shake with him.
Is he at home?"

"Why, no, then," she replied; "and if ever a man left in a fury
he did. It appears that someone told him of a big *bosthoon*
of a giant called Far Rua being down at the Causeway to look
for him, and so he set out there to try if he could catch him.
Troth, I hope, for the poor giant's sake, he won't meet with him,
for if he does Finn will make paste of him at once."

"Well," said the other, "I am Far Rua, and I have been seek-
ing him these twelve months, but he always kept clear of me;

and I will never rest day or night till I lay my hands on him."

At this Oonagh set up a loud laugh of great contempt, by the way, and looked at him as if he were only a mere handful of a man.

"Did you ever see Finn?" said she, changing her manner all at once.

"How could I?" said he. "He always took care to keep his distance."

"I thought so," she replied. "I judged as much; and if you take my advice, you poor-looking creature, you'll pray night and day that you may never see him, for I tell you it will be a black day for you when you do. But, in the meantime, you perceive that the wind's on the door, and as Finn himself is far from home, maybe you'd be civil enough to turn the house, for it's always what Finn does when he's here."

This was a startler, even to Far Rua; but he got up, however, and after pulling the middle finger of his right hand until it cracked three times, he went outside, and getting his arms about the house, completely turned it as she had wished. When Finn saw this he felt a certain description of moisture, which shall be nameless, oozing out through every pore of his skin; but Oonagh, depending upon her woman's wit, felt not a whit daunted.

"Arrah, then," said she, "as you're so civil, maybe you'd do another obliging turn for us, as Finn's not here to do it himself. You see, after this long stretch of dry weather that we've had, we feel very badly off for want of water. Now, Finn says there's a fine spring well somewhere under the rocks behind the hill there below, and it was his intention to pull them asunder; but having heard of you he left the place in such a fury that he never thought of it. Now, if you try to find it, troth, I'd feel it a kindness."

She then brought Far Rua down to see the place, which was then all one solid rock; and after looking at it for some time, he cracked his right middle finger nine times, and, stooping down, tore a cleft about four hundred feet deep and a quarter of a mile in length, which has since been christened by the name of Lumford's Glen. This feat nearly threw Oonagh herself off her guard; but what won't a woman's sagacity and presence of mind accomplish?

"You'll now come in," said she, "and eat a bit of such humble fare as we can give. Finn, even though you and he were enemies, would scorn not to treat you kindly in his own house; and, indeed, if I didn't do it even in his absence, he would not be pleased with me."

She accordingly brought him in, and placing half a dozen of the cakes we spoke of before him, together with a can or two of butter, a side of boiled bacon, and a stack of cabbage, she desired him to help himself — for this, be it known, was long before the invention of potatoes. Far Rua, who, by the way, was a glutton as well as a hero, put one of the cakes in his mouth to take a huge whack out of it, when both Finn and Oonagh were stunned with a noise that resembled something between a growl and a yell.

"Blood and fury!" he shouted out. "How is this? Here are two of my teeth out! What kind of bread is this you gave me?"

"What's the matter?" said Oonagh coolly.

"Matter!" shouted the other. "Why, here are two of the best teeth in my head gone."

"Why," said she, "that's Finn's bread — the only bread he ever eats when at home; but, indeed, I forgot to tell you that nobody can eat it but himself and that child in the cradle there. I thought, however, that as you were reported to be rather a stout little fellow of your size you might be able to manage it, and I did not wish to affront a man that thinks himself able to fight Finn. Here's another cake — maybe it's not so hard as that."

Far Rua, at the moment, was not only hungry, but ravenous, so he immediately made a fresh set at the second cake, and immediately another yell was heard twice as loud as the first.

"Thunder and giblets!" he roared. "Take your bread out of this, or I will not have a tooth in my head; there's another pair of them gone."

"Well, honest man," replied Oonagh, "if you're not able to eat the bread say so quietly, and don't be awakening the child in the cradle there. There now, he's awake upon me!"

Finn now gave a skirl that frightened the giant, as coming from such a youngster as he was represented to be.

"Mother," said he, "I'm hungry — get me something now to eat."

Oonagh went over, and putting into his hand a cake *that had no griddle in it* — Finn, whose appetite in the meantime was sharpened by what he saw going forward, soon made it disappear. Far Rua was thunderstruck, and secretly thanked his stars that he had the good fortune to miss meeting Finn, for, as he said to himself, I'd have no chance with a man who could eat such bread as that, which even his son that's in the cradle can munch before my eyes.

"I'd like to take a glimpse at the lad in the cradle," said he to Oonagh, "for I can tell you that the infant who can manage that nutriment is no joke to look at or to feed of a scarce summer."

"With all the veins of my heart," replied Oonagh. "Get up, acushla, and show this decent little man something that won't be unworthy of your father, Finn Mac Cool."

Finn, who was dressed for the occasion as much like a boy as possible, got up, and bringing Far Rua out, "Are you strong?" said he.

"Thunder and ounce!" exclaimed the other. "What a voice in so small a chap!"

"Are you strong?" said Finn again. "Are you able to squeeze water out of that white stone?" he asked, putting one into Far Rua's hand. The latter squeezed and squeezed the stone, but to no purpose; he might pull the rocks of Lumford's Glen asunder, and flatten a thunderbolt, but to squeeze water out of a white stone was beyond his strength. Finn eyed him with great contempt as he kept straining and squeezing and squeezing and straining till he got black in the face with the efforts.

"Ah, you're a poor creature," said Finn. "You a giant! Give me the stone here, and when I'll show what Finn's little son can do you may then judge of what my daddy himself is."

Finn then took the stone, and then, slyly exchanging it for the curds, he squeezed the latter until the whey, as clear as water, oozed out in a little shower from his hand.

"I'll now go in," said he, "to my cradle; for I scorn to lose my time with anyone that's not able to eat my daddy's bread, or squeeze water out of a stone. Bedad, you had better be off out of this before he comes back, for if he catches you, it's in flummery he'd have you in two minutes."

Far Rua, seeing what he had seen, was of the same opinion himself; his knees knocked together with the terror of Finn's return, and he accordingly hastened in to bid Oonagh farewell, and to assure her that, from that day out, he never wished to hear of, much less to see, her husband.

"I admit fairly that I'm not a match for him," said he, "strong as I am. Tell him I will avoid him as I would the plague, and that I will make myself scarce in this part of the country while I live."

Finn, in the meantime, had gone into the cradle, where he lay very quietly, his heart in his mouth with delight that Far Rua was about to take his departure without discovering the tricks that had been played off on him.

"It's well for you," said Oonagh, "that he doesn't happen to be here, for it's nothing but hawk's meat he'd make of you."

"I know that," said Far Rua, "divel a thing else he'd make of me; but, before I go, will you let me feel what kind of teeth they are that can eat griddle cakes like *that?*" and he pointed to it as he spoke.

"With all the pleasure in life," says she; "only as they're far back in his head you must put your finger a good way in."

Far Rua was surprised to find so powerful a set of grinders in one so young; but he was still much more so on finding, when he took his hand from Finn's mouth, that he had left the very finger upon which his whole strength depended behind him. He gave one loud groan and fell down at once with terror and weakness. This was all Finn wanted, who now knew that his most powerful and bitterest enemy was completely at his mercy. He instantly started out of the cradle, and in a few minutes the great Far Rua, that was for such a length of time the terror of him and all his followers, was no more.

Children of the Salmon

*T*HERE WAS a king in Ireland long ago, and neither he nor his wife had any children. Their dearest wish was to have a family, and so, one day he said to his wife:

"I will go to the Wise-Old-Blind-Man and ask his advice."

"Indeed do go and ask his advice, and maybe we will have children yet," said the queen.

He went to the Wise-Old-Blind-Man.

"Do you think there is anything at all that would help us to have a child?" he asked.

"There is, indeed," said the Wise-Old-Blind-Man. "Speak to the boatman, and ask him to get you a salmon. Get your cook to roast it for you, without a sign of burning or searing on it anywhere. Give that to your wife to eat, and no one else must eat any of it, and you will see that you will have a child."

The king went home, and he did as the Wise-Old-Blind-Man had told him. He got a salmon and he gave it to the cook, and she roasted it. There was a small burnt patch on the skin, she rubbed her finger over it, and she put her finger into her mouth to lick it. Three seasons from that night the cook had a young son, and the king's wife also had a young son on the same day.

The two children were reared together in the castle until they were old enough to go to school. They were sent to school then, and there was not one in the place, no matter how sharp his eyesight, that could tell the cook's son from the king's son, so alike they were in every way.

The queen liked to have the cook's son eat with her own son at their table, but she was never able to tell one of them from the other. So she said she would put a mark on the cook's son, to distinguish them, and one day, as they were coming back from school, she caught him and took the tip of the ear off him.

Next day, when they were going to school, the king's son said to the cook's son:

"Who took the tip of the ear off you?"

"Your mother, the queen did," said the cook's son, "so that when we are sitting at the same table she may know you from me."

"If that is the reason," said the queen's son, "you must take a snip off my ear too, just like the one that was taken off yours, and she will then be as puzzled as ever."

The cook's son took a snippet off the ear of the queen's son, and now the queen could not tell her son from the cook's son, but as little as ever.

The two youths continued going to school until they grew up into two fine young men. Then one day the cook's son said to the king's son:

"I have no business staying here any longer, I must go and seek my fortune."

"If you do," said the king's son, "I will go with you. Wherever one of us goes, let the other go too."

"Stay where you are," said the cook's son, "you have a good livelihood here. I will send you a sign, so that you will know whether I am dead or alive. If I am dead, a top of blood will come on the little well, and while I am alive there will be a top of honey on it."

CHILDREN OF THE SALMON

He went off then, and he took his hound, his dog and his
hawk with him. He kept going on and on, till he came to the
dwelling of a nobleman. He knocked at the hall door and a
servant girl opened it to him. He asked her was the master at
home, and she said he was. The nobleman came out and
asked him where he came from, and what did he want.

"I heard," said the cook's son, "that you were looking for a
servant boy, and I thought that maybe I would suit you."

"Good enough," said the nobleman. "Go in to the servant
girl and she will give you your supper. Tomorrow morning you
can go out herding the cattle."

So far so good. The cook's son got up early next morning. He
ate his breakfast and he went out herding the cattle. He soon
found that the place where they were to graze was as bare as the
road, and was without a blade of grass for them to eat. Over
the wall, at the side, there was a giant's garden, where there
was the best of grazing. "By my word," he said to himself, "I will
put them in there to graze, for there isn't a mouthful for cow
or calf in this place, and there is no use keeping them here."
So he made a gap in the wall then, and drove his cattle in to
graze in the giant's land. But if he did, they were not long
there when the giant came bounding up to him, and shouting:

"What are you doing here, and where are you from?"

"I am the King of Ireland's son, and I came here herding
these cattle."

"You are too big for one mouthful, and too small for two
mouthfuls, but if I put a grain of salt on you, I'd eat you in
one."

The giant then asked him whether he would prefer a bout of
wrestling or a bout of sword play, passing their blades in and out
through each other's ribs.

"I would prefer a contest in wrestling," said the cook's son, "so that my fine, noble bones will be on top of your churl's limbs."

They took a grip on each other then, and the first twist the giant gave to the cook's son, he put him down on one knee. Just then a beautiful maiden put her head out of the window of the courtyard, and said:

"O King of Ireland's son, there is none of your kith and kin here to lay you out, or to keen over you, if you are killed by the giant, so you had better get the upper hand of him."

He looked up at the maiden, and he got great courage. They started again then, and at the second bout the cook's son put the giant down on his knees.

"O King of Ireland's son," said the giant, "you are the best warrior that ever wrestled with me. Leave me my life, and I will give you my slender brown steed that can overtake the March wind in front of him, and who cannot be overtaken by the March wind that's behind him. And I will give you the Sword of Light, a sword that, if it does not kill with the first blow, will cleave to the marrow with the second."

"Where is it?" asked the cook's son.

"There it is, over there on the rock, take it with you," said the giant.

"I would like to try the sharpness of its edge," said the cook's son.

"Try it on that ugly old stump of wood behind you," said the giant.

"I do not see any old stump uglier than your own old stump," said the cook's son, striking the giant a blow on the neck, and taking the head off him. The head of the giant tried to get back on to his body again, but the cook's son hit it another blow and made two halves of it.

"It was well for you, you did that," said the head, "for if I

had got back on the same body again, half the Fianna of Ireland would not have been able to take me off it. I am finished
now."

"It serves you right!" said the cook's son.

Then the beautiful young maiden put her head out the
window again, and asked him to come in and eat his dinner at
the same table with her. She asked him then if he would
marry her, and he said he would. They got married then.
That was all very well, but that night, at twelve o'clock, a
hare came into the room where the cook's son was sleeping,
and struck him on the mouth with a dirty paw, and went out
again.

"I'll not put up with that," said the cook's son. "I'll find
that hare yet, or it will fail my best effort."

He got up and dressed himself then. He went out and took
with him his hound, his dog, his hawk and his slender brown
steed. They went off after the hare, and when the hare used to
be on the hill, they used to be in the glen, and when the hare
used to be in the glen, they used to be on the hilltop. The cook's
son was always and ever behind the hare, until the night
came. He saw a light then in the middle of a wood, and he drew
towards it. He walked on and on till he came to a little house
where the light was, and he walked in.

There was a fine fire blazing on the hearth, but there was not a
sign of anyone inside. He sat down by the fire to rest himself.
It wasn't long till he heard the door opening, and who should
come in, but a little, old, gray-haired hag. She sat down on the
floor near the door. He kept looking down at her, and wondering why she wasn't coming up to the fire.

"Why don't you draw up to the fire?" he asked her.

"I'm afraid of your hawk and your dogs," said she. "You
should tie them up."

"You need not be afraid of them," said he, "for they won't interfere with you at all."

"They would indeed," said she, "and you should tie them up."

"I have nothing to tie them up with," said the cook's son.

"I will give you the tying of them," said she. She drew three ribs of hair out of her head then, and gave them to him, saying: "Tie a rib around each dog's neck, and another around the head of the hawk."

He tied them up then, the hound, the dog and the hawk, and the old hag came up to the fire.

"What right have you to kill my son?" she said to him, and she took a fighting stand in front of him.

"Oh, you are the mother of the giant I killed yesterday," he said, and he got ready to defend himself from her talons that she stretched out before her. They attacked each other then in a hard, swift fight, until, after some time, the hag began to get the best of it.

"Help, help, hound!" the cook's son called out to his hound.

"Tighten, tighten, rib!" said the hag.

The rib of the hag's hair tightened on the hound's neck and choked him.

"Help, help!" said the cook's son.

"Tighten, tighten, rib!" said the hag.

"Wuff, wuff!" said the dog, and the rib tightened on his neck and choked him.

By this time the hag had the cook's son down on one knee.

"Help, help! Hawk, where are you?" said he.

"Tighten, tighten, rib!" said the hag.

The rib tightened and choked the hawk.

The hag then gave another twist to the cook's son, and got him down on his two knees.

"Oh, hag," he said, "you have the advantage of me now, and I am finished."

The hag then raised a magic wand and struck him, his hound, his dog, his hawk and his slender brown steed, and turned them into five gray standing stones.

So far so good. But the king's son, who had stayed at home, never let a night nor a morning pass that he did not go to the well to see whether his brother was dead or alive. The day the hag had put the cook's son under magic, the queen's son went to the well as usual, and he found that the top was blood, and underneath was honey.

"My brother is dead, or in danger," he said. "I will not eat the second meal, or drink the second drink, until I find my brother, dead or alive."

He went off then, and he took his hound, his dog and his hawk. Everywhere he went he asked for tidings of his brother, until he came to the house of the nobleman who hired him to herd his cattle, just as he had done with the cook's son.

The king's son ate his supper and he went to bed. He got up early in the morning. He ate his breakfast and he went out herding the nobleman's cattle. He found that there wasn't a blade of grass for them to eat, but as little as there was on the road.

"There isn't a bite for a gosling here," he said, "not to mind a cow. By my word, I think I will put them into this fine garden where they'll have the best of grazing," and he knocked a gap in the nearby wall and turned the cows into the giant's land.

It wasn't long until a great churl of a giant came running towards him.

"What brought you here," he asked, "and who are you?"

"That's no business of yours," said the king's son. "Send out my brother to me, dead or alive. I am the King of Ireland's son."

The giant tried to get a hold of him, to kill him, but the king's son leaped aside out of his grasp.

"You are too big for one bite, and too small for two bites, but if I had a grain of salt on you, I'd eat you in one mouthful. What way will you fight? Will you have a bout of wrestling, or a bout of sword play, with the blades going in and out between the ribs?"

"A bout of wrestling," said the king's son, "so that my fine, noble bones will be on top of your filthy, churlish ones."

They took grips on each other then, and the first twist that the king's son gave the giant he put him down on one knee. The beautiful maiden then put her head out through the window, and said:

"King's son from Ireland, there is no woman of your kin here to keen you, or to lay you out, so win the fight!"

When he heard this, he got greater strength, and the next twist he gave the giant he put him down on his two knees.

"Wait, wait," said the giant. "Leave my life with me and I will give you my slender brown steed and my Sword of Light. You are the best warrior I have ever met."

"Where is the Sword of Light?" asked the king's son.

"It is over there on the rock."

"What will I try it on?" asked the king's son.

"Try it on that old stump over there," said the giant.

"I do not see any stump older and uglier than yourself," said the king's son, and drawing a blow of the sword, he whipped the head off him, and made two halves of it.

"Bravo! Seven thousand lives to you!" said the beautiful maiden, out through the courtyard window. She asked him to come in then and to eat his dinner with her. He went in and ate his dinner at the same table with her. He went to bed then, and at twelve o'clock in the night, when he was asleep, a hare came into the room, and struck him on the mouth with her dirty paw, and off with her again.

He got up then, raging to get satisfaction from her, and he got his hound, his dog, his hawk and his slender brown steed, and he followed her. When the hare would be on the hill, they would be in the valley, and when they would be in the valley, the hare would be on the hill. The hunt went on till nightfall on the next day. Following a light he saw in the wood, he came to a small, mean little hut. He opened the door and went in. Who should be sitting by the fire, her head leaning on her hand, but an old hag.

"Get up," said the king's son, "and get my supper ready for me and my dogs."

"I would be afraid to stir," said she, "unless you tie them up, and that hawk, likewise."

"I have nothing to tie them with," said he, "and anyway they won't do you any harm."

"They would, indeed," said she, "and here's something to tie them with," and she drew three ribs of hair out of her head.

The king's son took the ribs of hair from the hag, and threw them into the fire when she was not looking.

"Get up now, and get my supper, quickly," he said.

"Indeed, I will not," said the hag.

"I'll make you get it for me," he said, drawing his Sword of Light.

The words were hardly out of his mouth when she caught a hold of him by the throat, and the two of them started to wrestle. The hag was getting the better of him, and she had him down on one knee, when he called out:

"Help, help! Hound!"

"Tighten, tighten, rib!" shouted the hag.

"I can't," said the rib, "for I am on the flat of my back in the fire."

The hound leaped up, and he took a bite out of the hag's face.

"Help! Help! Dog!" the king's son called.

"Tighten, tighten, rib!" shouted the hag.

"I can't, for I am on the flat of my back in the fire," said the rib.

The dog jumped on the hag, and took half her arm away with him.

"Help, help! Oh, hawk!" called the king's son.

"Tighten, tighten, rib!" called out the hag.

"I can't, for I am on the flat of my back in the fire," said the rib.

The hawk rose up and picked out one of the hag's eyes, and the king's son put her down on her back on the floor.

"Wait, wait!" she shouted. "Leave me my life, and I will give your brother back to you, with his hound, his dog, his hawk and his slender brown steed."

"Where are they?" he shouted at the hag.

"Take that magic wand over there, and strike a blow with it on the five gray stones outside the door, and they will stand up, as good as ever they were, day or night," said the hag.

"It is right that I should put you out of the world first," he said, as he tipped her with the wand and made a gray standing stone out of her. When he had that done, he touched the five standing stones with it, and his brother, with his hound, dog,

hawk and slender brown steed, rose up before him. The cook's
son and the king's son shook hands with each other then, and
each told the other of his adventures since they last met.

Both of them went back to the beautiful young woman at the
giant's castle. She gave her hand to the cook's son, and with it,
all the wealth of the giant, and he and she stayed on living in
the giant's castle for many a long day. The son of the King of
Ireland went home, and he married a daughter of the King of
France.

The Brown Bear of Norway

*T*HERE WAS once a king in Ireland, and he had three daughters, and very nice princesses they were. And one day that their father and themselves were walking on the lawn, the king began to joke on them, and to ask them whom they would like to be married to.

"I'll have the King of Ulster for a husband," says one; "and I'll have the King of Munster," says another; "and," says the youngest, "I'll have no husband but the Brown Bear of Norway."

For a nurse of hers used to be telling her of an enchanted prince that she called by that name, and she fell in love with him, and his name was the first name on her lips, for the very night before she was dreaming of him. Well, one laughed, and another laughed, and they joked on the princess all the rest of the evening. But that very night she woke up out of her sleep in a great hall that was lighted up with a thousand lamps; the richest carpets were on the floor, and the walls were covered with cloth of gold and silver, and the place was full of grand company, and the very beautiful prince she saw in her dreams was there, and it wasn't a moment till he was on one knee before her, and telling her how much he loved her, and asking her wouldn't she be his queen. Well, she hadn't the heart to refuse him, and married they were the same evening.

"Now, my darling," says he, when they were left by themselves, "you must know that I am under enchantment. A sorceress, that had a beautiful daughter, wished me for her son-in-law; and because I didn't keep the young girl at the distance I ought, the mother got power over me, and when I refused to marry her daughter, she made me take the form of a bear by day, and I was to continue so till a lady would marry me of her own free will and endure five years of great trials after."

Well, when the princess woke in the morning, she missed her husband from her side, and spent the day very sorrowful. But as soon as the lamps were lighted in the grand hall, where she was sitting on a sofa covered with silk, the folding doors flew open, and he was sitting by her side the next minute. So they spent another evening so happy, and he took an opportunity of warning her that whenever she began to tire of him, or not to have any confidence in him, they would be parted forever, and he'd be obliged to marry the witch's daughter.

So she got used to finding him absent by day, and they spent a happy twelvemonth together, and at last a beautiful little boy was born; and as happy as she was before, she was twice as happy now, for she had her child to keep her company in the day when she couldn't see her husband.

At last, one evening, when herself and himself and her child were sitting with a window open because it was a sultry night, in flew an eagle, took the infant's sash in his beak, and up in the air with him. She screamed, and was going to throw herself out through the window after him, but the prince caught her, and looked at her very seriously. She bethought of what he said soon after their marriage, and she stopped the cries and complaints that were on her lips. She spent her days very lonely for another twelvemonth, when a beautiful little girl was sent to her. Then she thought to herself she'd have a sharp eye about her this time; so she never would allow a window to be more than a few inches open.

But all her care was in vain. Another evening, when they were all so happy, and the prince dandling the baby, a beautiful greyhound bitch stood before them, took the child out of the father's hand, and was out of the door before you could wink. This time she shouted, and ran out of the room, and all declared that neither child nor dog passed out. She felt, she could not tell how to her husband, but still she kept command over herself, and didn't once reproach him.

When the third child was born, she would hardly allow a window or a door to be left open for a moment; but she wasn't the nearer to keeping the child to herself. They were sitting one evening by the fire when a lady appeared standing by them. She opened her eyes in a great fright, and stared at her, and while she was doing so, the appearance wrapped a shawl round the baby that was sitting in its father's lap, and either sunk through the ground with it, or went up through the wide chimney. This time the mother kept her bed for a month.

"My dear," said she to her husband, when she was beginning to recover, "I think I'd feel better if I was after seeing my father, and mother, and sisters once more. If you give me leave to go home for a few days, I'd be glad."

"Very well," said he, "I will do that; and whenever you feel inclined to return, only mention your wish when you lie down at night."

The next morning when she awoke, she found herself in her own old chamber in her father's palace. She rang the bell, and in a short time she had her mother, and father, and married sisters about her, and they laughed till they cried for joy at finding her safe back again.

So in time she told them all that happened to her, and they

didn't know what to advise her to do. She was as fond of her husband as ever, and said she was sure that he couldn't help letting
the children go; but still she was afraid beyond the world to
have another child to be torn from her. Well, the mother and
sisters consulted a wise woman that used to bring eggs to the
castle, for they had great confidence in her wisdom. She said
the only plan was to secure the bear's skin that the prince was
obliged to put on every morning, and get it burned, and then he
couldn't help being a man night and day, and then the enchantment would be at an end.

So they all persuaded her to do that, and she promised she
would; and after eight days she felt so great a longing to see her
husband again that she made the wish the same night, and
when she woke three hours after, she was in her husband's
palace, and himself was watching over her. There was great joy
on both sides, and they were happy for many days.

Now she began to reflect how she never felt her husband
leaving her of a morning, and how she never found him neglecting to give her a sweet drink out of a gold cup just as she
was going to bed.

So one night she contrived not to drink any of it, though she
pretended to do so; and she was wakeful enough in the morning, and saw her husband passing out through a panel in the
wainscot, though she kept her eyelids nearly closed. The next
night she got a few drops of the sleepy posset that she saved the
evening before, put into her husband's night drink, and that
made him sleep sound enough. She got up after midnight,
passed through the panel, and found a beautiful brown bear's
hide hanging in an alcove. She stole back, and went down to
the parlor fire, and put the hide into the middle of it, and never
took eyes off it till it was all fine ashes. She then lay down

by her husband, gave him a kiss on the cheek, and fell asleep.

If she was to live a hundred years, she'd never forget how she wakened next morning, and found her husband looking down on her with misery and anger in his face.

"Unhappy woman," said he, "you have separated us forever! Why hadn't you patience for five years? I am now obliged, whether I like or not, to go a three days' journey to the witch's castle, and live with her daughter. The wife that gave you the counsel was the witch herself. I won't reproach you: your punishment will be severe enough without it. Farewell forever!"

He kissed her for the last time, and was off the next minute, walking as fast as he could. She shouted after him, and then seeing there was no use, she dressed herself and pursued him. He never stopped, nor stayed, nor looked back, and still she kept him in sight; and when he was on the hill she was in the hollow, and when he was in the hollow she was on the hill. Her life was almost leaving her, when just as the sun was setting, he turned up a *bohyeen* (lane), and went into a little house. She crawled up after him, and when she got inside there was a beautiful little boy on his knees, and he kissing and hugging him.

"Here, my poor darling," says he, "is your eldest child, and there," says he, pointing to a nice middle-aged woman that was looking on with a smile on her face, "is the eagle that carried him away."

She forgot all her sorrows in a moment, hugging her child, and laughing and crying over him. The Vanithee washed their feet, and rubbed them with an ointment that took all the soreness out of their bones, and made them as fresh as a daisy. Next morning, just before sunrise, he was up, and prepared to be off.

"Here," said he to her, "is a thing which may be of use to you. It's a scissors, and whatever stuff you cut with it will be

turned into rich silk. The moment the sun rises, I'll lose all
memory of yourself and the children, but I'll get it at sunset
again; farewell."

But he wasn't far gone till she was in sight of him again, leaving her boy behind. It was the same today as yesterday; their
shadows went before them in the morning, and followed them in
the evening. He never stopped, and she never stopped, and as the
sun was setting, he turned up another lane, and there they
found their little daughter. It was all joy and comfort again till
morning, and then the third day's journey commenced.

But before he started, he gave her a comb, and told her that
whenever she used it, pearls and diamonds would fall from her
hair. Still he had his full memory from sunset to sunrise; but
from sunrise to sunset he traveled on under the charm, and
never threw his eye behind. This night they came to where the
youngest baby was, and the next morning, just before sunrise,
the prince spoke to her for the last time.

"Here, my poor wife," said he, "is a little hand reel, with gold
thread that has no end, and the half of our marriage ring. If you
can ever get to my bed, and put your half ring to mine, I will
recollect you. There is a wood yonder, and the moment I enter
it, I will forget everything that ever happened between us, just
as if I was born yesterday. Farewell, dear wife and child, forever."

Just then the sun rose, and away he walked towards the
wood. She saw it open before him, and close after him, and
when she came up, she could no more get in than she could
break through a stone wall. She wrung her hands, and shed
tears, but then she recollected herself, and cried out:

"Wood, I charge you by my three magic gifts — the scissors,
the comb, and the reel — to let me through"; and it opened,
and she went along a walk till she came in sight of a palace, and

a lawn, and a woodman's cottage in the edge of the wood where it came nearest the palace.

She went into this lodge and asked the woodman and his wife to take her into their service. They were not willing at first; but she told them she would ask no wages, and would give them diamonds, and pearls, and silk stuffs, and gold thread whenever they wished for them. So they agreed to let her stay.

It wasn't long till she heard how a young prince, that was just arrived, was living in the palace as the husband of the young mistress. Herself and her mother said that they were married fifteen years before, and that he was charmed away from them ever since. He seldom stirred abroad, and everyone that saw him remarked how silent and sorrowful he went about, like a person that was searching for some lost thing.

The servants and conceited folk at the big house began to take notice of the beautiful young woman at the lodge, and to annoy her with their impudent addresses. The head footman was the most troublesome, and at last she invited him to *come take tea* with her. Oh! How rejoiced he was, and how he bragged of it in the servants' hall! Well, the evening came, and the footman walked into the lodge, and was shown to her sitting-room; for the lodge keeper and his wife stood in great awe of her, and gave her two nice rooms to herself. Well, he sat down as stiff as a ramrod, and was talking in a grand style about the great doings at the castle while she was getting the tea and toast ready.

"Oh," says she to him, "would you put your hand out of the window and cut me off a sprig or two of honeysuckle?"

He got up in great glee, and put out his hand and head; and said she:

"By the virtue of my magic gifts, let a pair of horns spring out of your head, and serenade the lodge."

Just as she wished, so it was. They sprang from the front of each ear, and tore round the walls till they met at the back. Oh, the poor wretch! And how he bawled, and roared! And the servants that he used to be boasting to were soon flocking from the castle, and grinning, and huzzaing, and beating tunes on tongs, and shovels, and pans; and he cursing and swearing, and the eyes ready to start out of his head, and he so black in the face, and kicking out his legs behind like mad.

At last she pitied his case and removed the charm, and the horns dropped down on the ground, and he would have killed her on the spot, only he was as weak as water, and his fellow servants came in and carried him up to the big house.

Well, some way or other, the story came to the ears of the prince, and he strolled down that way. She had only the dress of a country woman on her as she sat sewing at the window, but that did not hide her beauty, and he was greatly puzzled and disturbed, after he had a good look at her features, just as a body is perplexed to know whether something happened to him when he was young, or if he only dreamed it. Well, the witch's daughter heard about it too, and she came to see the strange girl; and what did she find her doing, but cutting out the pattern of a gown from brown paper; and as she cut away, the paper became the richest silk she ever saw. The lady looked on with very covetous eyes, and, says she:

"What would you be satisfied to take for that scissors?"

"I'll take nothing," says she, "but leave to spend one night in the prince's chamber, and I'll swear that we'll be as innocent of any crime next morning as we were in the evening."

Well, the proud lady fired up, and was going to say something dreadful; but the scissors kept on cutting, and the silk growing richer and richer every inch. So she agreed, and made her take a great oath to keep her promise.

When night came on she was let into her husband's chamber, and the door was locked. But, when she came in a-tremble, and sat by the bedside, the prince was in such a sleep that all she did couldn't wake him. She sung this verse to him, sighing and sobbing, and kept singing it the night long, and it was all in vain:

> "Four long years I was married to thee;
> Three sweet babes I bore to thee;
> Brown Bear of Norway, won't you turn to me?"

At the first dawn, the proud lady was in the chamber, and led her away, and the footman of the horns put out his tongue at her as she was quitting the palace.

So there was no luck so far; but the next day the prince passed by again, and looked at her, and saluted her kindly, as a prince might a farmer's daughter, and passed on; and soon the witch's daughter came by and found her combing her hair, and pearls and diamonds dropping from it.

Well, another bargain was made, and the princess spent another night of sorrow, and she left the castle at daybreak, and the footman was at his post, and enjoyed his revenge.

The third day the prince went by and stopped to talk with the strange woman. He asked her could he do anything to serve her, and she said he might. She asked him did he ever wake at night. He said that he was rather wakeful than otherwise; but that during the last two nights he was listening to a sweet song in his dreams and could not wake, and that the voice was one that he must have known and loved in some other world long ago. Says she:

"Did you drink any sleepy posset either of these evenings before you went to bed?"

"I did," said he. "The two evenings my wife gave me something to drink, but I don't know whether it was a sleepy posset or not.

"Well, prince," says she, "as you say you would wish to oblige me, you can do it by not tasting any drink this afternoon."

"I will not," says he, and then he went on his walk.

Well, the great lady was soon after the prince, and found the stranger using her hand reel and winding threads of gold off it, and the third bargain was made.

That evening the prince was lying on his bed at twilight, and his mind much disturbed; and the door opened, and in his princess walked, and down she sat by his bedside, and sung:

> "Four long years I was married to thee;
>   Three sweet babes I bore to thee;
>   Brown Bear of Norway, won't you turn to me?"

"Brown Bear of Norway!" said he. "I don't understand you."

"Don't you remember, prince, that I was your wedded wife for four years?"

"I do not," said he, "but I'm sure I wish it was so."

"Don't you remember our three babes, that are still alive —"

"Show me them. My mind is all a heap of confusion."

"Look for the half of our marriage ring that hangs at your neck, and fit it to this."

He did so, and the same moment the charm was broken. His full memory came back on him, and he flung his arms round his wife's neck, and both burst into tears.

Well, there was a great cry outside, and the castle walls were heard splitting and cracking. Everyone in the castle was alarmed, and made their way out. The prince and princess went with the rest, and by the time all were safe on the lawn, down came the building, and made the ground tremble for miles around. No one ever saw the witch and her daughter afterwards. It was not long till the prince and princess had their children with them, and then they set out for their own palace. The kings of Ireland and of Munster and Ulster, and their wives, soon came to visit them, and may everyone that deserves it be as happy as the Brown Bear of Norway and his family.

Animal Stories

The Cock

W HEN THEY buried Jesus Christ they killed a cock and put him down in a pot to boil, and they said that Jesus would rise from the dead as soon as the cock would rise up out of the pot. Very soon the cock got up and stood on the edge of the pot and crowed twelve times. They knew then that the Son of God had risen. When the cock shook his wings and crowed what he said was: "The Son of God is living!"

The Flounder

W HEN Saint Columba got ashore on the white strand of Iona,
a flounder raised his head out of the water and said in derision:
"O Columcille of the hoary-head!" Columcille made reply: "If
I am a hoary-head may you be a wry-mouth, and may your two
eyes be on the one temple."

The Strengths of the Cat

THE cat once had a shilling. He paid fourpence for the absent-mindedness of the woman of the house. He paid fourpence to be able to see as well in the dark as in the light. And he paid the third fourpence to be able to walk without making the slightest noise, so that he can pounce on, and catch, anything that stirs.

The Eyesight of the Pig

*T*HE pig has the best eyesight of any animal. The first night the moon comes no one, except the pig, can see it.

No one sees it on the second night either, except the pig. On the third night everyone sees it.

The pig can see the wind too, for her eyes are as narrow as a silken thread.

The Old Crow and the Young Crow

*T*HERE WAS an old crow teaching a young crow one day, and he said to him, "Now, my son," says he, "listen to the advice I'm going to give you. If you see a person coming near you, and stooping, mind yourself, and be on your keeping; he's stooping for a stone to throw at you."

"But tell me," says the young crow, "what should I do if he had a stone already down in his pocket?"

"Musha, go 'long out of that," says the old crow, "you've learned enough; the divel another learning I'm able to give you."

The Cat's Place by the Fire

*F*ROM BYGONE times the dog used always be out in the cold and the wet while the cat was always inside cosy by the fireside. One day when the dog was drowned and wet from the rain he said to the cat: "You are fine and comfortable inside always while I'm out in the cold and wet, but I'm going to see to it that you'll not be inside any longer."

The man of the house heard the argument between them, so he thought he'd better settle the matter. "Tomorrow, I'll put you both to race against one another — five miles from the house and back, and the one that will come in first will have the place inside by the fire, and the other will have to stay outside."

So the two got ready and they ran the race, and on the way back the dog was half a mile ahead of the cat. A tramp coming along the road thought the dog was going to bite him when he saw him coming with his mouth open so he gave him a blow of a stick he had in his hand. When the dog felt the blow he stopped and began to bark at the tramp and made to bite him, to get satisfaction from him.

All this time the cat was quietly making her way home, and when the dog arrived at last she was sitting at her ease in front of the fire licking herself.

"Now," says she to the dog, "I've won the race, and the place inside by the fire is mine forevermore."

The Wren, the King of the Birds

ALL THE birds of the air came together one time to see which of them could fly farthest up in the air. And as they all gathered together on one hill the little wren was so small that not one of them noticed him, and he was able to hide himself in between two downy feathers in the eagle's back. Then they all rose in the air and went up and up, to see who would fly the highest, and they spent five nights and five days rising straight up into the sky. Only a few of the birds lasted that long, but the eagle was one of them. Then at last when he had gone up as far as he was able to go he said that he had won, for he was the highest. He called out three times that he was the highest up in the sky, and then he began to come down.

When the wren saw that the eagle was not able to go any higher he flew out of his hiding place among the eagle's feathers, and he rose three or four feet up over him.

"You have not won," said the wren.

"Where were you?" asked the eagle. "I never saw a bit of you coming up."

"I was very close to you," said the wren, "but I was unseen by you."

"You have won the day!" said the eagle. "You are the King of the Birds."

The wren has been king ever since.

The Fox, the Otter and the Wolf

T HE FOX and the otter and the wolf went fishing one night, west to Curraghgallerus. The fox and the wolf used to watch for the fish, and if they saw a trout the otter would dive in and catch it.

They were not getting any fish and it began to freeze hard.

"Here," said the fox, "let each of us put his tail down into the water, and maybe a trout will come and we'll get a bite."

Each of them put his tail down into the water as the fox said, and they were fishing in that way for a long time, but if they were they got no bites. The fox drew his tail up out of the water after a while. "Oh," said he, "I thought a trout was biting me, but he must have gone off. I'll try again."

He put his tail down into the water again like the others, but he started drawing it up every now and then so as to keep it from getting stuck in the hard ice that was forming around them. The other two remained sitting on the bank and with their two tails down in the water and not stirring, but no fish came to bite them. All the time the fox kept on moving his tail out of the water every so often.

In the end he told the otter and the wolf to draw up their tails, since there was no likelihood of getting any bites. They tried to draw them up but they couldn't stir them. They tried and tried again but it was little use for them, their tails were caught fast in the ice. In the end they got tired of trying.

When the fox saw that they were not able to stir, he jumped on them and killed them both. He went away then west to Ballyranna, shouting "Tobacco! Tobacco! Tobacco!"

The Cockroach

WHEN THE Son of God was fleeing from His enemies He passed by a field where a man was planting oats. On the following day the oats were ripe and ready for cutting. The man did not think that enough time had passed since the oats were planted to have them ready for cutting already. However, he went to the field on the following day and began to cut the oats. As he was working the Jews went past, and they asked him if he had seen the Son of God pass by there. He told them he had seen Him go by when he was sowing the oats.

"That was yesterday! Yesterday! Yesterday!" said the cockroach.

"That's a lie! That's a lie! That's a lie!" said the beetle.

There is no one who sees a cockroach ever since who does not put his foot down on it to kill it. But the beetle is blessed and no one kills it.

The Bonny Bunch of Blackberries

ONE DAY a widow woman was sweeping the floor and she found a silver sixpence. She went to the fair and she bought a kid with the sixpence. On the way home from the fair, as she drove the kid along, she saw a bonny bunch of blackberries growing by the roadside. She was very tired and she thought she would sit down on a grassy bank that was there while she ate the blackberries.

So she said to the kid: "Kid, kid, go over the bridge till I sit down and eat my bonny bunch of blackberries."

"I will not," said the kid.

She went along till she met a dog, and she said to the dog: "Dog, dog, bite kid. Kid won't go over the bridge till I sit down and eat my bonny bunch of blackberries."

"I will not," said the dog, "the kid never did me any harm."

She went along till she met a stick, and she said to the stick: "Stick, stick, beat dog, dog won't bite kid, kid won't go over the bridge till I sit down and eat my bonny bunch of blackberries."

"I will not," said the stick, "the dog never did me any harm."

She went along till she met a fire, and she said to the fire: "Fire, fire, burn stick, stick won't beat dog, dog won't bite kid, kid won't go over the bridge till I sit down and eat my bonny bunch of blackberries."

"I will not," said the fire, "the stick never did me any harm."

She went along till she met a pool of water, and she said to the water: "Water, water, quench fire, fire won't burn stick, stick won't beat dog, dog won't bite kid, kid won't go over the bridge till I sit down and eat my bonny bunch of blackberries."

"I will not," said the water, "the fire never did me any harm."

She went along till she met a cow, and she said to the cow: "Cow, cow, drink water, water won't quench fire, fire won't burn stick, stick won't beat dog, dog won't bite kid, kid won't go over the bridge till I sit down and eat my bonny bunch of blackberries."

"I will not," said the cow, "the water never did me any harm."

She went along till she met a butcher, and she said to the butcher: "Butcher, butcher, kill cow, cow won't drink water, water won't quench fire, fire won't burn stick, stick won't beat dog, dog won't bite kid, kid won't go over the bridge till I sit down and eat my bonny bunch of blackberries."

"I will not," said the butcher, "the cow never did me any harm."

She went along till she met a rope, and she said to the rope: "Rope, rope, hang butcher, butcher won't kill cow, cow won't drink water, water won't quench fire, fire won't burn stick, stick won't beat dog, dog won't bite kid, kid won't go over the bridge till I sit down and eat my bonny bunch of blackberries."

"I will not," said the rope, "the butcher never did me any harm."

She went along till she met a rat, and she said to the rat: "Rat, rat, gnaw rope, rope won't hang butcher, butcher won't kill cow, cow won't drink water, water won't quench fire, fire won't burn stick, stick won't beat dog, dog won't bite kid, kid won't go

THE BONNY BUNCH OF BLACKBERRIES

over the bridge till I sit down and eat my bonny bunch of black-berries."

"I will not," said the rat, "the rope never did me any harm."

She went along till she met a cat, and she said to the cat: "Cat, cat, catch rat, rat won't gnaw rope, rope won't hang butcher, butcher won't kill cow, cow won't drink water, water won't quench fire, fire won't burn stick, stick won't beat dog, dog won't bite kid, kid won't go over the bridge till I sit down and eat my bonny bunch of blackberries."

"Miaou!" said the cat. "Where's the rat?"

> Then the cat began to eat the rat,
> The rat began to gnaw the rope,
> The rope began to hang the butcher,
> The butcher began to kill the cow,
> The cow began to drink the water,
> The water began to quench the fire,
> The fire began to burn the stick,
> The stick began to beat the dog,
> The dog began to bite the kid,
> And the kid ran over the bridge,

And the old woman sat down and ate her bonny bunch of black-berries.

The Cat and the Mouse

*T*HERE WAS a cat and a mouse-*een* playing one day, and the cat snapped the tail off the mouse.

"Give me my tail*een*," said the mouse.

"I'll do that," said the cat, "if you bring me a drop of milk from the heifer."

"Heifer, give me a drop [of milk], till I give a drop to the cat*een*, till the cat*een* gives me my tail*een*."

"I'll do that," said the heifer, "if you bring me a wisp from the barn."

"Barn, give me a wisp till I give a wisp to the heifer, till the heifer gives me a drop [of milk] to give to the cat*een*, till the cat*een* gives me my tail*een*."

"I'll do that," said the barn, "if you bring me a key from the smith."

"Smith give me a key to give to the barn, till the barn gives me a wisp, till I give a wisp to the heifer, till the heifer gives me a drop, till I give a drop to the cat*een*, till the cat*een* gives me my tail*een*."

"I'll do that," says the smith, "if you bring me a cake from the breadwoman."

"Breadwoman, give me a cake to give to the smith, till the smith gives me a key, till I give a key to the barn, till the barn gives me a wisp, till I give a wisp to the heifer, till the heifer gives me a drop, till I give a drop to the cat*een*, till the cat*een* gives me my tail*een*."

"I'll do that," said the breadwoman, "if you bring me a sieve of water from the river."

She went to the river, she got the sieve and she thrust it down and lifted it up, and the water ran through it.

There passed by a copper-red robin*een* of O'Sullivan's people, who said:

"Put yellow clay and marl at the bottom of your sieve." The mouse did as she was told. Then she thrust down the sieve into the river and lifted it up full of water, and she gave the water to the breadwoman.

> The breadwoman gave a cake to the mouse*een*,
> The mouse-*een* gave a cake to the smith,
> The smith gave a key to the mouse-*een*,
> The mouse-*een* gave a key to the barn,
> The barn gave the mouse-*een* a wisp,
> The mouse-*een* gave a wisp to the heifer,
> The heifer gave a drop [of milk] to the mouse-*een*,
> The mouse-*een* gave a drop to the cat*een*, and when the
> Cat*een* had the drop drunk she ate the mouse-*een*!

That is my story and if there's a lie in it let it be so.

How the First Cat Was Created

ONE DAY Mary and her Son were traveling the road and they were heavy and tired. It chanced that they passed the door of a house where there was a lock of wheat being winnowed. The Blessed Virgin went in and she asked for an alms of wheat, and the woman of the house refused her.

"Go in to her again," said the Son, "and ask her for it in the name of God."

She went, and the woman refused her again.

"Go in to her again," said the Son, "and ask her to give you leave to put your hand into the pail of water, and to thrust it down into the heap of wheat, and to take away with you all that shall cling to your hand."

She went and the woman gave her leave to do that. When she came out to our Saviour, He said to her, "Do not let one grain of that go astray, for it is worth much and much."

When they had gone a bit from the house they looked back and saw a flock of demons coming towards it, and the Virgin Mary was frightened lest they should do some harm to the woman. "Let there be no anxiety on you," said Jesus to her, "since it has chanced that she has given you all that of alms, they shall get no victory over her."

They traveled on then till they reached as far as a place where a man named Martin had a mill. "Go in," said the

Saviour to His mother, "since it has chanced that the mill is working, and ask them to grind that little grain-*een* for you."

She went. "Oh musha, it's not worthwhile for me," said the boy who was attending the querns, "to put the little *lockeen* [stone] a-grinding for you."

Martin heard them talking, and said to the lout: "Oh, then do it for the creature, perhaps she wants it badly," said he. He did it, and gave her all the flour that came from it.

They traveled on then, and they were not gone any distance until the mill was full of flour as white as snow. When Martin perceived this great miracle he understood well that it was the Son of God and His mother that chanced that way. He ran out and followed them, at his best, and he made across the fields until he came up with them, and there was that much haste on him going through a sconce of hawthorns that a spike of the hawthorn met his heart and wounded him greatly. There was that much zeal in him that he did not feel the pain, but clapt his hand over it and never stopped till he came up with them. When our Saviour beheld the wound upon poor Martin, He laid His hand upon it and it was closed and healed upon the spot. He said to Martin that he was a fitting man in the presence of God and "Go home now," said He, "and place a fistful of the flour under a dish, and do not stir it until morning."

When Martin went home he did that, and he put the dish, mouth under, and a fistful of flour beneath it.

The servant girl was watching him and thought that it would be a good thing if she were to set a dish for herself in the same way, and signs on her, she set it.

On the morning of the next day Martin lifted his dish, and what should run out from under it but a fine sow and a big litter of *bonhams* (piglets) with her. The girl lifted her own dish and there ran out a big mouse and a clutch of young mouselets with her. They ran here and there, and Martin at once thought that they were not good, and he plucked a mitten off his hand and flung it at the mice. As soon as it touched the ground it changed into a cat, and the cat began to kill the young mice. That was the beginning of cats.

Martin was a saint from that time on, but I do not know which of the saints he was of all that were called Martin.

Jack and His Comrades

ONCE THERE was a poor widow, and there often was, and she had one son. A very scarce summer came, and they didn't know how they would live till the new potatoes would be fit for eating. So Jack said to his mother one evening, "Mother, bake my cake, till I go seek my fortune; and if I meet it, never fear but I'll soon be back to share it with you." So she did as he asked her, and he set out at break of day on his journey.

His mother came along with him to the *bawn* (lawn) gate, and says she, "Jack, which would you rather have, half a cake and half a cock with my blessing, or the whole of 'em with my curse?"

"O musha, Mother," says Jack, "why do you ax me that question? Sure you know I wouldn't have your curse and Damer's* estate along with it."

"Well then, Jack," says she, "here's the whole *tote* [lot] of 'em, and my thousand blessings along with them." So she stood on the bawn ditch (fence) and blessed him as far as her eyes could see him.

Well, he went along and along till he was tired, and ne'er a farmer's house he went into wanted a servant boy. At last his road led up by the side of a bog, and there was a poor ass up

---

* A rich Dublin moneylender, contemporary with Dr. Jonathan Swift, commemorated by him in an appropriate lament. Damer is to the Irish peasant what Croesus was to the old Greeks.

to his shoulders near a big bunch of grass he was striving to come at. "Ah, then, Jack asthore," says he, "help me out or I'll be drownded." "Never say't twice," says Jack, and he pitched in big stones and *scraws* (sods) into the slob, till the ass got good ground under him. "Thank you, Jack," says he, when he was out on the hard road; "I'll do as much for you another time. Where are you going?" "Faith, I'm going to seek my fortune till harvest comes in, God blessit!" "And if you like," says the ass, "I'll go along with you; who knows what luck we may have!" "With all my heart; it's getting late, let's be jogging."

Well, they were going through a village, and a whole army of gorsoons (boys) were hunting a poor dog with a kittle tied to his tail. He ran up to Jack for protection, and the ass let such a roar out of him that the little thieves took to their heels as if the ould boy (the devil) was after them. "More power to you, Jack," says the dog. "I'm much obliged to you; where is the baste and yourself going?" "We're going to seek our fortune till harvest comes in." "And wouldn't I be proud to go with you!" says the dog, "and get shut of them ill-conducted boys; *purshuin* to 'em!" "Well, well, throw your tail over your arm, and come along."

They got outside the town, and sat under an old wall, and Jack pulled out his bread and meat and shared with the dog; and the ass made his dinner on a bunch of thistles. While they were eating and chatting, what should come by but a poor, half-starved cat, and the moll-row he gave out of him would make your heart ache. "You look as if you saw the tops of nine houses since breakfast," says Jack; "here's a bone and something on it." "May your child never know a hungry belly!" says Tom. "It's myself that's in need of your kindness. May I be so bold as to ask where yous are all going?" "We're going to seek our fortune till the harvest comes in, and you may join us if you like." "And that I'll do with a heart and a half," says the cat, "and thank'ee for asking me."

Off they set again, and just as the shadows of the trees were three times as long as themselves, they heard a great crackling in a field inside the road, and out over the ditch jumped a fox with a fine black cock in his mouth. "Oh you anointed villian!" says the ass, roaring like thunder. "At him, good dog!" says Jack, and the word wasn't out of his mouth when Coley was in full sweep after the *Moddhera Rua* (Red Dog). Reynard dropped his prize like a hot potato, and was off like a shot, and the poor cock came back fluttering and trembling to Jack and his comrades. "O musha, neighbors," says he, "wasn't it the height of luck that threw you in my way! Maybe I won't remember your kindness if ever I find you in hardship; and where in the world are you all going?" "We're going to seek our fortune till the harvest comes in; you may join our party if you like, and sit on Neddy's crupper when your legs and wings are tired."

Well, the march began again, and just as the sun was gone down they looked around, and there was neither cabin nor farm house in sight. "Well, then," says Jack, "the worse luck now the better another time, and it's a summer night after all. We'll go into the wood and make our beds on the long grass." No sooner said than done. Jack stretched himself out on a bunch of dry grass, the ass lay near him, the dog and the cat lay in the ass's warm lap, and the cock went to roost in the next tree.

Well, the soundness of deep sleep was over them all, when the cock took a notion of crowing. "Bother you, *Cuileach Dhu* [Black Cock]!" says the ass. "You disturbed me from as nice a wisp of hay as ever I tasted. What's the matter?" "It's daybreak that's the matter: don't you see light yonder?" "I see a light indeed," says Jack, "but it's from a candle it's coming, and not from the sun. As you've roused us we may as well go over and ask for lodging." So they all shook themselves, and went on through grass, and rocks, and briars till they got down into a hollow, and there was the light coming through the shadow, and along with it came singing, and laughing, and cursing. "Easy boys!" says Jack. "Walk on your tippy toes till we see what sort of people we have to deal with." So they crept near the window, and they saw six robbers inside, with pistols, and blunder-bushes, and cutlashes, sitting at a table, eating roast beef and pork, and drinking mulled beer, and wine, and whiskey punch.

"Wasn't that a fine haul we made at the Lord of Dunlavin's!" says one ugly-looking thief with his mouth full. "And it's little we'd get only for the honest porter: here's his pretty health!" "The porter's pretty health!" cried out every one of them, and Jack bent his finger at his comrades. "Close your ranks, my men," says he in a whisper, "and let everyone mind the word of com-mand." So the ass put his forehoofs on the sill of the window, the dog on the ass's head, the cat on the dog's head, and the cock on the cat's head. Then Jack made a sign and they all sung out like mad. "Hee-haw, hee-haw!" roared the ass; "Bow-wow!" barked the dog; "Miaou! miaou!" cried the cat; "Cock-a-doodle-doo!" crowed the cock. "Level your pistols!" cried Jack. "And make smithereens of 'em. Don't leave a mother's son of 'em alive; present, fire!" With that they gave another halloo, and smashed every pane in the window. The robbers were frightened out of their lives. They blew out the candles, threw down the table, and skelped out the back door as if they were in earnest, and never drew rein till they were in the very heart of the wood.

Jack and his party got into the room, closed the shutters, lighted the candles, and ate and drank till hunger and thirst were gone. Then they lay down to rest; Jack in the bed, the ass in the stable, the dog on the doormat, the cat by the fire, the cock on the perch.

At first the robbers were very glad to find themselves safe in the thick wood, but they soon began to get vexed. "This damp grass is very different from our warm room," says one; "I was obliged to drop a fine pig's *crubeen* [pig's foot]," says another; "I didn't get a tayspoonful of my last tumbler," says another; "and all the Lord of Dunlavin's goold and silver that we left behind!" says the last. "I think I'll venture back," says the captain, "and see if we can recover anything." "That's a good boy!" said they all, and away he went.

The lights were all out, and so he groped his way to the fire, and there the cat flew in his face and tore him with teeth and claws. He let a roar out of him, and made for the room door, to look for a candle inside. He trod on the dog's tail, and if he did, he got the marks of his teeth in his arms, and legs, and thighs. "*Millia murdher* [thousand murders]!" cried he. "I wish I was out of this unlucky house."

When he got to the street door, the cock dropped down upon him with his claws and bill, and what the cat and the dog had done to him was only a flaybite to what he got from the cock. "Oh, Tattheration to you all, you unfeeling vagabones!" says he, when he recovered his breath; and he staggered and spun round and round till he reeled into the stable, back foremost, but the ass received him with a kick on the smallest part of his small clothes, and laid him comfortably on the dunghill. When he came to himself, he scratched his head and began to think what had happened to him; and as soon as he found that his legs were able to carry him, he crawled away, dragging one foot after another, till he reached the wood.

"Well, well," cried them all, when he came within hearing, "any chance of our property?" "You may say chance," says he, "and it's itself is the poor chance all out. Ah, will any of you pull a bed of dry grass for me? All the sticking-plaster in Inniscorfy (Enniscorthy) will be too little for the cuts and bruises I have on me. Ah, if you only knew what I have gone through for you! When I got to the kitchen fire, looking for a sod of lighted turf, what should be there but a *colliach* [old woman] carding flax, and you may see the marks she left on my face with the cards. I made to the room door as fast as I could, and who should I stumble over but a cobbler and his seat, and if he did not work at me with his awls and his pinchers you may call me a rogue. Well, I got away from him somehow, but when I was passing through the door, it must be the divel himself that pounced down on me with his claws and his teeth, that were equal to sixpenny nails, and his wings — ill luck be in his road! Well, at last I reached the stable, and there, by way of salute, I got a pelt of a sledgehammer that sent me half a mile off. If you don't believe me, I'll give you leave to go and judge for yourselves."

"Oh, my poor captain," says they, "we believe you to the nines. Catch us, indeed, going within a hen's race of that unlucky cabin!"

Well, before the sun shook his doublet next morning, Jack and his comrades were up and about. They made a hearty breakfast of what was left the night before, and they all agreed to set off to the castle of the Lord of Dunlavin, and give him back all his gold and silver. Jack put it all in the two ends of a sack, and laid it across Neddy's back, and all took the road in their hands. Away they went, through bogs, up hills, down dales, and sometimes along the yalla high road, till they came to the hall door of the Lord of Dunlavin, and who should be there, airing his powdered head, his white stockings, and his red breeches, but the thief of a porter.

He gave a cross look to the visitors and says he to Jack, "What do you want here my fine fellow? There isn't room for you all."

"We want," says Jack, "what I'm sure you haven't to give us —
and that is common civility." "Come, be off, you lazy *geochachs*
[greedy strollers]!" says he. "While a cat 'ud be licking her ear,
or I'll let the dogs at you." "Would you tell a body," says the
cock that was perched on the ass's head, "who was it that
opened the door for the robbers the other night?" Ah, maybe the
porter's red face didn't turn the color of his fringe and the Lord
of Dunlavin and his pretty daughter, that were standing at the
parlor window unknownst to the porter, put out their heads.
"I'll be glad, Barney," says the master, "to hear your answer to
the gentleman with the red comb on him." "Ah, my poor lord,
don't believe the rascal; sure I didn't open the door to the six
robbers." "And how did you know there were six, you poor innocent?" said the lord. "Never mind, sir," says Jack, "all your
gold and silver is there in that sack, and I don't think you will
begrudge us our supper and bed after our long march from the
wood of Athsalach [muddy ford]." "Begrudge, indeed! Not one
of you will ever see a poor day if I can help it."

So all were welcomed to their heart's content, and the ass, and
the dog, and the cock got the best posts in the farmyard, and
the cat took possession of the kitchen. The lord took Jack in
hand, dressed him from top to toe in broadcloth, and frills as
white as snow, and turn-pumps, and put a watch in his fob.
When they sat down to dinner, the lady of the house said Jack
had the air of a born gentleman about him, and the lord said
he'd make him his steward. Jack brought his mother and settled
her comfortable near the castle, and all were as happy as you
please. The old woman that told me the story said that Jack and
the young lady were married; but if they were, I hope he spent
two or three years getting the edication of a gentleman. I don't
think that a country boy would feel comfortable striving to find
discourse for a well-bred young lady the length of a summer's

day, even if he had the *Academy of Compliments* and the *Complete Letter Writer** by heart.

* Two chap or pedlar's books, great favorites among our people during the last century.

The Grateful Beasts

THERE WAS once a young man, and it happened that he had a
guinea in his pocket, and was going to some fair or *pattern** or
another, and while he was on the way he saw some little boys
scourging a poor mouse they were catching. "Come gorsoons,"
says he, "don't be at that cruel work; here's sixpence for you to
buy gingerbread and let him go." They only wanted the wind
of the word, and off jumped the mouse. He hadn't gone much
farther when he overtook another parcel of young *geochachs*,
and they tormenting the life out of a poor weasel. Well, he
bought him off for a shilling, and went on. The third creature
he rescued from a crowd of grown-up young rascals was an
ass, and he had to give a whole half crown to get him off. "Now,"
says poor Neddy, "you may as well take me with you, I'll be some
use carrying you when you're tired." "With all my heart," says
Jack. The day was very hot, and the boy sat under a tree to enjoy the cool. As sure as he did he fell asleep without intending
it, but he was soon woke up by a wicked looking *bodach* (churl)
and his two servants. "How dare you let your ass to trespass on
my *inch* [river meadow]" says he, "and do such mischief." "I
had no notion he'd do anything of the kind; I dropped asleep
by accident." "Oh, be this an' that! I'll accidence you. Bring

* *pattern*: feast held on a Saint's day.

340

out that chest," says he to one of his *gillas* (menservants), and while you'd be saying thrapsticks they had the poor boy lying on the broad of his back in it, and a strong hempen rope tied round it, and himself and itself flung into the river.

Well, they went away to their business, and poor Neddy stayed roarin' and bawlin' on the bank, till who should come up but the weasel and the mouse, and they axed him what ailed him. "An' isn't it the kind boy that rescued me from them scoggins [buffoons] that were tormenting me just now, fastened up in a chest and dhrivin' down that terrible river?" "Oh," said the weasel, "he must be the same boy that rescued the mouse and myself. Had he a brown piece on the elbow of his coat?" "The very same." "Come then," said the weasel, "and let us overtake him, and get him out." "By all means," said the others. So the weasel got on the ass's back and the mouse in his ear, and away with them. They hadn't gone far when they saw the chest stopped among the rushes at the edge of a little island. Over they went, and the weasel and the mouse gnawed the rope till they had the lid off, and their master out on the bank. Well, they were all very glad, and were conversing together, then what did the weasel spy but a beautiful egg with the loveliest colors on the shell lying down in the shallow water. It wasn't long till he had it up, and Jack was turning it round and round, and admiring it. "Oh musha, my good friends," says he, "I wish it was in my power to show my gratitude to you, and that I had a fine castle and estate where we could live with full and plenty!" These words were hardly out of his mouth when the beasts and himself found themselves standing on the steps of a castle, and the finest lawn before it that ever you saw.

There was no one inside or outside to dispute possession with them, and they lived as happy as kings. They found money enough inside in a cupboard, and the house had the finest fur-

niture in every room, and it was an easy matter to hire servants
and laborers.

Jack was standing at his gate one day as three merchants were
passing by with their goods packed on the backs of horses and
mules. "Death alive!" says they. "What's this for? There was
neither castle, nor lawn, nor tree here the last time we went by."

"True for you," says Jack. "But you won't be the worse for it.
Take your beasts into the bawn, behind the house, and give
'em a good feed, and if you're not in a hurry, stay and take a
bit of dinner with myself." They wished for no better, and after
dinner the innocent slob of a Jack let himself be overtaken, and
showed them his painted egg, and told 'em everything that had
happened to him. As sure as the hearth money, one of 'em
puts a powder in Jack's next tumbler, and when he woke it was
in the island he found himself, with his patched coat on him,
and his three friends sitting on their *currabingoes* (hunkers)
near him, looking very down in the mouth. "Ah master," says
the weasel, "you'll never be wise enough for the tricky people
that's in this world. Where did them thieves say they lived, and
what is the name that's on 'em?" Jack scratched his head and
after a little while he recollected the town. "Come, Neddy," says
the weasel, "let's be jogging." So he got on his back, and the
mouse in his ear, and the ass swum the river, and nothing is said
of their travels till they came to the house of the head rogue. The
mouse went in, and the ass and the weasel sheltered themselves
in a copse outside. He soon came back to them. "Well, what
news?" "Dull news enough. He had the egg in a low press in his
bedroom, and a pair of cats with fiery eyes watching it night and
day, and they chained to the press, and the room door double-
locked."

"Let's go back," says the ass, "we can't do nothing." "Wait,"
says the weasel.

When sleep time came, says the weasel to the mouse, "Go in at the keyhole, and get behind the rogue's head, and stay two or three hours sucking his hair." "What good is that?" says the ass. "Wait an' you'll know," says the weasel. Next morning the merchant was mad to find the way his hair was. "But I'll disappoint you tonight, you thief of a mouse," says he. So he unchained the cats next night, and bid them sit by his bedside and watch.

Just as he was dropping asleep, the weasel and the mouse were outside the door, and gnawing away till they had a hole scooped out at the bottom. In went the mouse and it wasn't long till he had the egg outside. They were soon on the road again, the mouse in the ass's ear, and the weasel on his back, and the egg in the weasel's mouth. When they came to the river, they were swimming across when the ass began to bray: "Hee-haw, hee-haw!" says he. "Is there the likes of me in the world? I'm carrying the mouse and the weasel, and the great enchanted egg that can do anything. Why don't yous praise me?" But the mouse was asleep, and the weasel was afraid of opening his mouth. "I'll shake yous off, you ungrateful pack, if you don't," says the ass again, and the poor weasel, forgetting himself, cried out: "Oh don't!" And down went the egg in the deepest pool in the river. "Now you done it," says the weasel, and you may be sure the ass looked very lewd (ashamed) of himself.

"Oh, what are we to do now, at all, at all," says he. "Never despair," says the weasel. He looked down into the deep water and cried: "Hear all you frogs and fish! There is a great army coming to take yous out, and eat yous red raw; look sharp!" "Oh what can we do?" says they coming up to the top. "Gather up all the stones and hand them to us, and we'll make a big wall on the bank to defend you."

They began to work like little divels in a mud wall, and were hard and fast reaching up the pebbles they found on the bottom. At last a big frog came up with the egg in his mouth, and when the weasel had hold of it, he got up in a tree, and cried out: "That will do, the army is frightened and running away." So the poor things were greatly relieved.

You may be sure that Jack was very rejoiced to see his friends and the egg again. They were soon back in their castle and lawn, and when Jack began to feel lonesome he did not find it hard to make out a fine young wife for himself, and he and his friends were as happy as the day was long.

Notes

THE FAIRY HOST (*The Slua Shee*)

SOURCE: Padraig O'Laoghaire in *The Gaelic Journal,* Vol. IV.

WHERE BILL KEANE LIT HIS PIPE

DID THE TAILOR GET THE THREAD YET?

THE VACANT COW BAIL

SOURCE: *Béaloideas,* Vol. IV, No. iii, pp. 278-284. Collected by Martin Burke, Ait Aoibhinn, South Douglas Road, Cork.

MIDNIGHT RACES

THE MAGIC SHIP

SOURCE: *Béaloideas,* Vol. II, No. 1, pp. 77-80. Collected by the late Séan O'Dubhda, Tralee, Co. Kerry.

THE SOW TAKEN BY THE FAIRIES

THE DANCE IN BALLYCUMBER

THE FAIRY DINNER

THE CARDPLAYER AND THE FAIRIES

SOURCE: *Béaloideas,* Vol. VII, No. I, pp. 87-92. Collected by Pádraig O'Tuathail (School teacher), Hacketstown, Co. Carlow.

THE STORY OF NORA MACKAY AND THE FAIRIES

SOURCE: From oral tradition, told by Seamus O'Muiris. Eanac Cuan, Co. Galway, and taken down by C. P. Bushe. *The Gaelic Journal,* Vol. IV.

FAIRY COWS

SOURCE: *Tales of the Irish Fairies,* by Jeremiah Curtin. David Nutt. London, 1896.

THE FAIRY CHILD

THE FAIRY NURSE

THE KILDARE LURIKEEN

SOURCE: *Legendary Fictions of the Irish Celts,* by Patrick Kennedy. Macmillan and Company, London, 1866.

PAUDYEEN O'KELLY AND THE WEASEL

SOURCE: *Beside the Fire,* by Douglas Hyde. David Nutt, London, 1890.

THE LEGEND OF BOTTLE HILL

SOURCE: *Fairy Legends of Ireland,* by Crofton Croker. George Allen and Co., London, 1888.

CEATACH AND BLACKBIRD

SOURCE: Told by Blake, of Ballinrobe, taken down by Douglas Hyde (An Craoibhin Aoibhinn) and published in Gaelic in *Béaloideas,* Vol. I, No. II, pp. 141-150.

KING OF LIES

SOURCE: *Sgéaluidheacht Chuige Mumhan,* by Padraig O'Laoghaire. The Gaelic League, Dublin, 1895.

BLAIMAN, SON OF APPLE, IN THE KINGDOM OF THE WHITE STRAND

SOURCE: *Hero Tales of Ireland,* collected and edited by Jeremiah Curtin. Macmillan and Co., London, 1894.

THE WIDOW'S SON AND THE WIZARD

SOURCE: *Imtheachtai an Oireachtais,* 1899, edited by S. J. Barrett.

NARRATOR: John MacDermot, Carrowmore, Tuam, Co. Galway. Written down in Gaelic by Michael O'Reilly. Shrule, Tuam, Co. Galway.

LIAM DONN

SOURCE: *Béaloideas,* Vol. I, No. I, pp. 290-296.

NARRATOR: Padraig O'Gabhain. Casla, Connemara. Written down in Gaelic by Peadar O'Griobhtha (schoolteacher), Connemara.

THE TREACHEROUS EAGLE

SOURCE: *Sgéaluidheacht Chuige Mumhan,* by Pádraig O'Laoghaire. The Gaelic League, Dublin, 1895. In this tale the storyteller's memory faltered in giving the details of a well-known motif at the end. I confess to having filled it out from a story, "The King's Son and the Eagle's Daughter," told to Curtin by one of the Kerry storytellers, who was living about twenty-five miles away from O'Laoghaire. This is the sole occasion on which I had to resort to what might be called "plastic surgery."

THE APPRENTICE THIEF

THE BLACKSMITH

PETER MEGRAB AND HIS BROTHER JOHN

SOURCE: *The Royal Hibernian Tales,* a rare, early nineteenth-century chap book, "One of the rarest books in Irish folklore." It is mentioned by Thackeray in his *Irish Sketch Book,* of 1842: "The eighteenpenny worth of little books purchased at Ennis in the morning came here most agreeably to my aid . . . These books are prepared for the people chiefly, and have been sold for many years before the march of knowledge began to banish Fancy out of the world . . ." *The Royal Hibernian Tales* (only a few copies extant) were once sold at fairs and markets for a penny or two. Now fortunately they have been preserved from extinction by the Irish Folklore Institute and are to be found reprinted in *Béaloideas,* Vol. X, No. II, pp. 148-203.

THE ADVENTURES OF THE FARMER AND THE RED WIZARD

SOURCE: *The Gaelic Journal,* Vol. IV, p. 7.
NARRATOR: Padraig O'Brien, Dublin (given in Gaelic).

MOIREEN

SOURCE: *Imtheachtai an Oireachtais,* 1890. Also in *Trí Sgéalta,* edited by Douglas Hyde. The Gaelic League, Dublin, 1895.

SHAWN MACBREOGAN AND THE KING OF THE WHITE NATION

SOURCE: *Hero Tales of Ireland,* collected by Jeremiah Curtin. Macmillan and Co., London, 1894.

THE KING'S SON WHO WOULD NOT OBEY

SOURCE: *The Gaelic Journal,* Vol. VII, p. 89.
NARRATOR: Michael Doohan. Fanad, Co. Donegal. Written down in Gaelic by J. N. Deeney. Franad, Co. Donegal.

THE DAUGHTER OF THE KING OF GREECE
SOURCE: *Imtheachtai an Oireachtais,* 1899, edited by S. J. Barrett. The Gaelic League, Dublin.
NARRATOR: Timothy O'Connor. Knockduff, Millstreet, Co., Cork. Written down in Gaelic by John M. Kiely. Cuilin, Millstreet, Co. Cork.

A LEGEND OF KNOCKMANY
SOURCE: *Traits and Stories of the Irish Peasantry,* by William Carleton. William Tegg, London, 1879.

CHILDREN OF THE SALMON
SOURCE: *Imtheachtai an Oireachtais,* 1899, edited by S. J. Barrett.
NARRATOR: Michael MacDermot. Shrule, Tuam, Co. Galway. Written down in Gaelic by Michael O'Reilly. Shrule, Tuam, Co. Galway.

THE BROWN BEAR OF NORWAY
SOURCE: *Legendary Fictions of the Irish Celts,* by Patrick Kennedy. Macmillan and Co., London, 1866.

THE COCK
SOURCE: *Béaloideas,* Vol. IV, No. I, p. 74.

THE FLOUNDER
SOURCE: *Béaloideas,* Vol. II, No. II, p. 228.

THE STRENGTHS OF THE CAT
SOURCE: *Béaloideas,* Vol. V, No. II, p. 249.

THE EYESIGHT OF THE PIG
SOURCE: *Béaloideas,* Vol. V, No. II, p. 249.

THE OLD CROW AND THE YOUNG CROW
THE CAT'S PLACE BY THE FIRE
SOURCE: *Béaloideas,* Vol. III, No. II, p. 495.

THE WREN, THE KING OF THE BIRDS
SOURCE: *Béaloideas,* Vol. III, No. II, p. 498.

THE FOX, THE OTTER AND THE WOLF
SOURCE: *Béaloideas,* Vol. III, No. II, p. 253.

THE COCKROACH
SOURCE: *Béaloideas,* Vol. V, No. II, p. 249.

THE BONNY BUNCH OF BLACKBERRIES is from personal memory.

THE CAT AND THE MOUSE

SOURCE: *Béaloideas,* Vol. I, No. I, p. 61. Collected by Douglas Hyde.

HOW THE FIRST CAT WAS CREATED

SOURCE: *The Religious Songs of Connacht,* by Douglas Hyde, London, 1906.

JACK AND HIS COMRADES

SOURCE: *Legendary Fictions of the Irish Celts,* collected and told by Patrick Kennedy. Macmillan and Co., London, 1866.

THE GRATEFUL BEASTS

SOURCE: *Fireside Stories of Ireland,* collected and told by Patrick Kennedy. Macmillan and Co., London, 1860.